C0-AUA-715

SO LONG, PLASTIC!

We've had a good run, we've shared some great memories,
but our time together has come to an end. It's not you, it's us.
Oh wait, it is you! ... or is it both of us?

BEYONDPLASTIC is an initiative and affair of the heart
created by Ulrich Krzyminski.

Plast...

[æl·kə'] ...
Plaster/Pow...
material used a...
coating of walls a...
and casting decorative...

An imprecise term use...
is stucco, which is also...
plasterwork that is worked in...
produce relief decoration, rat...
surfaces.

Plastoholic / Plastoholi...

[æl·kə'hɔ·lɪk]
1. (noun, m/f)) A perso...
single-use plastic.
2. (adjective) The...
much single-use ...
Also Plastaholi...
Pastaholism,...
insatiable p...

Plastoh...
in our ...
Pollu...
ob...
b...

using too much

behavior using too

be confounded with >
type of addiction; the
delicious pasta dishes.

...un) is widely spread nowadays
-Away Society. It leads to > Plastic
...ich is the accumulation of plastic
nd particles (e.g. plastic bottles,
microbeads) in the Earth's environment
...versely affects wildlife, wildlife habitat,
humans.

...ample text: Peter and Mary are serious
Plastoholics. They buy all their food and
toiletries in plastic packages and eat their lunch
out of plastic boxes which they simply throw
away after use. Studies show that people who overcome
Plastoholism successfully are more balanced
with nature and live a more responsible, healthy
and harmonious life. They follow the motto
Reduce-Reuse-Recycle and believe in a circular
economy.

Bec...
few hu...
given its...
and is a major...

Pocahontas
(1595 - 1616), Daughter...
Powhatan located in the...
Chickahominy River is the be...
best-known traditions connecte...
of North American history.

Poe, Edgar Allen
(/pou/; born Edgar Poe; Janu...
October 7, 1849). American w...
and literary critic, best known...
short stories, particularly his t...
and the macabre. He is widely
central figure of Romanticism
States and of American li...
and he was one of
generally consi...
practitioners of...
fiction ge...
contrib...
fict...

Plata, Río de la
Spanish pronunciation: [ˈri.o ðe la ˈplata])
broad estuary, approximately 171 mi...
between Argentina and Urug...
ports and capital cit...
...tevideo and flow...

MANIFESTO

We are BEYONDPLASTIC and we are on a mission to rid the world of single-use plastics.

For centuries we have packaged our goods with beautiful materials such as paper, cardboard, or organic fibers that are quiet in sync with nature. Then, around 70 years ago, a magical new substance conquered our consumer life — you guessed it, plastic! This 'magic material' quickly gave engineers an abundant playground to create extravagant products at a low manufacturing cost.

The dark side? We became a throw-away society and started to pollute the world with our plastoholic behavior. Our obsession with this 'magic material' is a short-sighted amour fou; we made it and made it and made it some more without a single thought about what happened when we no longer needed it. Like those plastic lids for the coffee-to-go cups for example, which are used for a couple of minutes and then remain in the world for hundreds of years. Plastics pollute the land, flow from the rivers to the sea where they degrade slowly into teeny-tiny particles, which are toxically absorbed by plants and animals and may return in the food on our tables. As the old saying goes: "You always meet twice in life."

Over recent decades we have transformed Planet Earth into a waste dump of plastic trash. And it gets bigger and bigger every minute, every hour, every day. Not forgetting that plastic is made from limited fossil resources that puts stress on the climate, but we'll save that conversation for another day.

And finally, there is the fact that many plastic products lack the aesthetic and haptic qualities other natural materials offer. We don't condemn plastic in total and thanks to its functional characteristics it can make sense to use it for long-lasting products. However, for short-duration, single-use products such as packaging, we do not think it is a good choice.

We believe there should be fewer plastics in the world. In particular less single-use plastic packaging.

It's time to say so long, my dear plastics!

BEYONDPLASTIC
www.beyondplastic.net
hello@beyondplastic.net
@beyondplastic_

Scan the code within the
Spotify App to listen to our podcast:

Let us design and create eco-responsible products and packages. Let us transform plastic products into solutions made of environmentally sound materials.

HOW THE JOURNEY BEGAN

My professional background lies in the print and packaging industry, so I am used to being surrounded by natural materials such as paper and cardboard. Over the years I saw more and more plastic entering the packaging sector which, in most cases, I don't favor for environmental and aesthetic reasons.

I started to investigate the ecological problems caused by single-use plastic and to evaluate possible solutions. On this journey, I discovered that there are many creative people all over the world passionately engaged in working on brilliant ideas for a world with less plastic. They come from all different disciplines: Material Science, Design, Environmental Engineering, Biology, Arts, Journalism.

I decided to create a platform where these people can present and exchange their wonderful ideas, concepts, products, and initiatives. BEYONDPLASTIC was born.

As an Engineer and Entrepreneur, I like navigating the overlapping creative terrain of art and science. I also like to explore our rich cultural history and combine it with modern technology in order to create sustainable solutions.

The good news about our adventure towards a plastic-less future is this – everything is already there! Generations of bright minds have laid the foundations of a century-old rich culture in manufacturing and using natural and eco-responsible materials. Let's rediscover it, mingle it with our new know-how and technology and start a plastic-less product and packaging renaissance!

At BEYONDPLASTIC we unite people who work together for a world with less plastic.

Join our movement!

Let us work together for a world with Less Plastic!

Ulrich Krzyminski
Founder of BEYONDPLASTIC

**Celebrating the excellence
in eco-responsible product & packaging design
across the world ...**

THE AWARD

The BEYONDPLASTIC Award honors the innovation and creativity in sustainable design in four categories:

I.   Most Innovative approach
II. Most Practical impact to reduce the use of plastics
III. Most Beautiful solution
IV. Best Initiative in Education / Journalism / Campaigning

For each category, there is a Gold, Silver, and Bronze Award.

The competition is directed towards students, designers, engineers, makers, creators, inventors, artists. Everyone who has an idea, concept, project, prototype, or even a solution already in the market which supports less single-use plastic is welcome to take part.

It can either be an entry that replaces an existing non-environmentally friendly product or package, or it can be a completely new solution. It can also be a campaign, educational or journalism project related to the topic. No idea is too crazy. As the co-founder of Google, Larry Page, said: "Good ideas are always crazy until they are not."

The Entries are judged by an expert Jury Panel who evaluates how well the following criteria are met, considering:

Is it eco-responsible? To use? To manufacture? Is it reusable? Is it recyclable? Is it biodegradable? Does it save resources and energy? Is it useful? Does it work well? Is it easy to understand? Is it practical? Can it be repairedwell? Is it beautiful? Is it elegant? Is it aesthetic? Is it clear and distinctive? Is it interesting? Is the idea thought-provoking? Is it original? Is it unique? Is it innovative? Clever? Brilliant? Ingenious?

When we ran the BEYONDPLASTIC Award for the first time in 2020 we had no idea what to expect in terms of the quality and quantity of Entries. We were thrilled to receive 107 Entries, from which the Jury Panel selected 85 awesome Nominations and amongst them awarded 13 Winners from all over the world contributing to a world with less plastic.

Thank you everyone for making this happen. We hope you enjoy browsing through the following pages.

Let us celebrate the excellence and awesomeness in eco-responsible product and packaging design and initiatives using less plastic across the world!

AWARD ENTRIES FROM ALL OVER THE WORLD

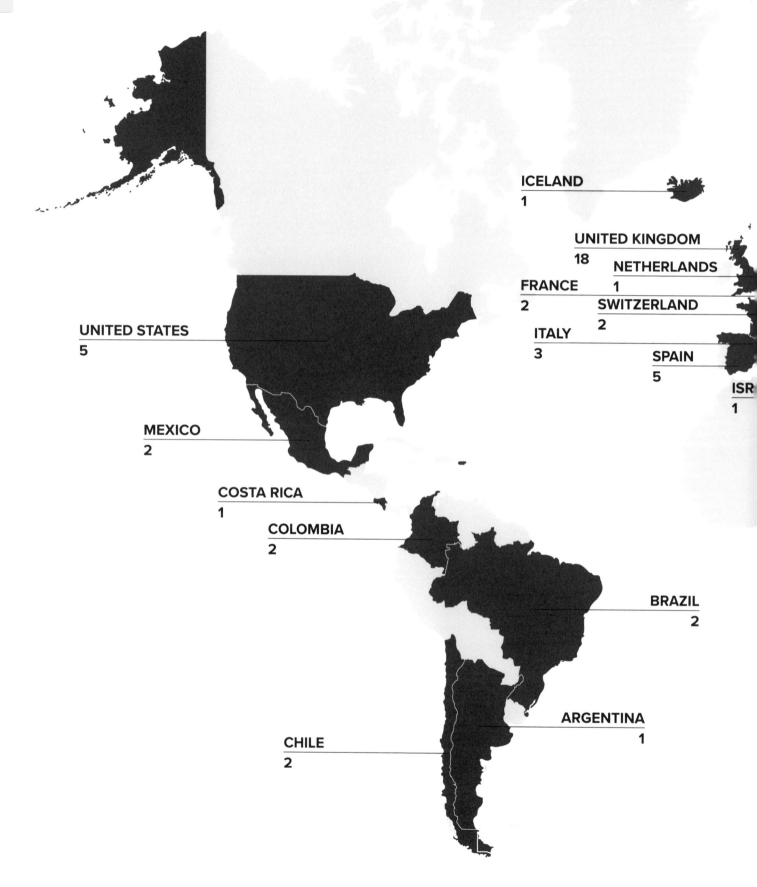

ICELAND
1

UNITED KINGDOM
18

NETHERLANDS
1

FRANCE
2

SWITZERLAND
2

ITALY
3

SPAIN
5

ISR
1

UNITED STATES
5

MEXICO
2

COSTA RICA
1

COLOMBIA
2

BRAZIL
2

ARGENTINA
1

CHILE
2

SWEDEN
1

DENMARK
1

GERMANY
16

AUSTRIA
5

BULGARIA
1

CYPRUS
2

TED ARAB EMIRATES

JAPAN
1

INDIA
3

SOMALIA
1

INDONESIA
1

ZAMBIA
2

AUSTRALIA
1

NEW ZEALAND
1

MOST INNOVATIVE SOLUTIONS

In this category, we present solutions for a world with less plastic which are novel, clever, unique, brilliant, inventive, edgy, visionary, offbeat, creative, cutting edge, thought-provoking, ground-breaking, out-of-the-box, above & beyond, progressive, forward-thinking and trendsetting.

14

this is no ordinary bag.
it will dissolve in fresh or salt water and leave no microplastics behind. it's also biodegradable, non-toxic and carbon negative.

the item bag 2.0 by **wastebased**.co
re-use this bag as many times as you can, then remove all labels, place it in boiling water, stir and it will dissolve in a matter of seconds. please exercise caution when handling boiling water.

WARNING
to avoid danger of suffocation, keep this bag away from babies and children. do not use this bag in cribs, beds, carriages or playpens. this bag is not a toy.

this is no ordinary bag.
it will dissolve in fresh or salt water and leave no microplastics behind. it's also biodegradable, non-toxic and carbon negative.

the item bag 2.0 by **wastebased**.co
re-use this bag as many times as you can, then remove all labels, place it in boiling water, stir and it will dissolve in a matter of seconds. please exercise caution when handling boiling water.

WARNING
to avoid danger of suffocation, keep this bag away from babies and children. do not use this bag in cribs, beds, carriages or playpens. this bag is not a toy.

WASTEBASED, UNITED KINGDOM

This Is No Ordinary Bag

Polybags are a huge ecological problem in the fashion industry. They're normally made from polyethylene or polypropylene and they're used for storing clothing as it moves around the supply chain. Almost every piece of clothing goes in a polybag at some point, and often items will move from polybag to polybag as they make their way to the consumer, resulting in a lot of invisible plastic consumption behind the scenes. Even brands trying their hardest to be sustainable are facing difficulties removing polybags from their supply chains entirely. But polybags do have a purpose. Products need to be stored safely as they travel from manufacturer to consumer and handled without damaging delicate fabrics. At Wastebased they have been working hard to upgrade the polybag, and their solution is the Item Bag 2.0 – a biodegradable, non-toxic, carbon-negative storage bag made from a polymer similar to the material used to coat dishwasher/laundry tablets, that dissolves in boiling water in seconds. You can dispose of it by dissolving it in boiling water almost instantly! The resulting solution contains mineralized biomass and non-toxic ink and can be directly poured down the sink. The best part is that the bag is effectively carbon-negative: Each bag offsets 200 % of the carbon footprint, so each one is drawing CO_2 out of our atmosphere instead of adding to it. What makes the founders of Wastebased most excited is that the Item Bag 2.0 is easily accessible to small and medium-sized brands who wish to start implementing this technology right now!

GOLD AWARD WINNER
Carla Perez, Jack Cleary & The Wastebased Team,
Wastebased, United Kingdom

Coffee Talk with Jack & Carla

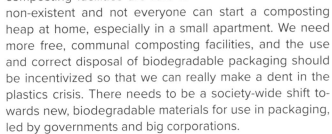

Tell us in a few words: Who are you? What do you do? We're Jack and Carla, the co-founders of Wastebased. We're on a mission to make sustainable packaging accessible and affordable to anyone who wants it.

What motivated you to get into sustainability? We've both wanted to make careers in sustainability for a long time, but it was only in 2018 that we made the jump. We felt overwhelmed by the sheer amount of single-use, disposable plastic that we, as a society, consumed on a daily basis – for takeaway coffee and food, produce, online orders, and personal care products. Plastic packaging from online orders was piling up in our house and we felt like nothing was being done about it, so we took the matter into our own hands.

How did you come up with your idea? It was very hard for us to order anything online that wasn't wrapped or padded with plastic. We knew online shopping was only going to increase so we looked for solutions. Most plastics can technically be recycled, but in practice, aren't. We thought there had to be another alternative (other than cardboard boxes) – something light and waterproof. We've always loved gardening and when we discovered that compostable plastic was out there, we knew it was the answer.

What are your future plans for your project? The e-commerce industry is growing exponentially and compostable plastics still make up only a tiny fraction of all plastic packaging used so we're working hard to bring to market new compostable and water-soluble alternatives to help with that!

What are the biggest obstacles you face? Our society is still not optimized for composting. We're hopefully just at the beginning of the composting revolution. Communal composting facilities are rare to non-existent and not everyone can start a composting heap at home, especially in a small apartment. We need more free, communal composting facilities, and the use and correct disposal of biodegradable packaging should be incentivized so that we can really make a dent in the plastics crisis. There needs to be a society-wide shift towards new, biodegradable materials for use in packaging, led by governments and big corporations.

What do you think we can do to solve the plastic pollution problem? This needs to happen at an international and governmental level. Plastic bans are needed, new materials need to be researched and developed, and innovative start-ups need to be incentivized. But if the cry for change doesn't start with us today, we could be waiting a long time for that to happen. Also: reduce, reduce, reduce as much as possible! And when there's no option but to use plastic, reuse something you already have, or use products made of materials that can be composted or recycled.

THE SHELLWORKS, UNITED KINGDOM

The Story of a Lobster Shell

Only 9% of all plastics globally are recycled. 92% of all biodegradable polymers require a similar infrastructure to recycling, called industrial composting, which hasn't been successful – when these biodegradable polymers end up in the wrong waste stream they cause just as much harm as traditional plastics.

The Shellworks creates packaging for the cosmetic, beauty, fashion, and retail industries from food waste. Their first products are bottle caps, jars and pots, and secondary packaging (trays, boxes). They make these products from biopolymers that are created from food waste. The Shellworks' secondary packaging products such as trays and boxes are made from Chitosan, an abundant polysaccharide found within shellfish waste.

Their value proposition: 1. Waste as input: 90% of the product is made from waste sources such as shellfish waste, food waste, or waste fibers. 2. It does not require consumer behavior change.

The founders aim to create impact by scaling their operations as quickly as possible to replace as much plastic-based packaging as possible.

To measure their impact, the start-up has four key metrics: 1. Measure how much plastic is replaced. 2. Measure how much waste is repurposed. 3. Quantify how much faster The Shellworks material degrades compared to other plastics. 4. Document a Life Cycle Analysis to ensure sustainable decisions are made across the supply chain.

SILVER AWARD WINNER
Insiya Jafferjee, Amir Afshar, Edward Jones,
The Shellworks, United Kingdom

Coffee Talk with Insiya ⬤ ᐧ|ᐧ|ᐧ|||ᐧ|||ᐧ||||ᐧ|

Please, tell us a little about yourself, who you are, and what you do. I grew up in Sri Lanka and then I went to study in California. I studied Mechanical and Manufacturing Engineering just because I really liked to know how things are made. However, I felt like something was missing and I wanted to do something more meaningful. And so I came to do my master's at the Royal College of Art in London. And that's where I met my two co-founders Edward and Amir and that's how The Shellworks started. Right now, we're working on creating natural alternatives to plastic packaging by extracting a biopolymer from shellfish waste and using that to make plastic alternatives.

How did you come up with the initial idea to use shellfish material? I think we were all interested in looking at how we could make an ecological impact. It was during a group project that we did during our masters where we started looking at waste materials and the deeper we looked into it, we found that fish waste is an area that's overlooked. We decided to focus fully on that area and went from there. The project evolved gradually and we tried to change certain things, or we tried to scale up the manufacturing process. We're driven by essentially being uncompromising in creating materials that will degrade in any environment. We started by collecting shells from restaurants in London and doing experiments in the lab. What we found was the main gap between a lot of these biodegradable polymers and the truly degradable ones, is that they're quite difficult to manufacture.

What are the plans for The Shellworks? We are getting ready for commercial production. We started doing some pilots using new manufacturing methods, which are much more scalable, and so I hope to see our products in the market by the middle of next year. The two biggest areas of impact are cosmetic packaging and food packaging. Because the products interact with our bodies, people are more conscious about making decisions that are good for the environment and also good for them. Additionally, with natural cosmetics, a lot of companies are already shifting to using all-natural ingredients, so sustainable packaging is the last piece of completing that narrative to consumers.

What do you think we can all do to fight the plastic problem on a large scale? It's a massive problem and I think it has to be tackled by a lot of different stakeholders. There's the consumer side of it, which comes through education. A lot of consumers are trying to deal with the problem on an individual basis. There's also the business side of it. There are now many more alternatives coming on the market and greenwashing has been a problem in the past. A lot of businesses are cautious to move to new materials or change the material that they're using right now. There's a bit of a complex process within that, but I think it's required. Finally, there's what the government has been doing, which has been really promising in introducing either tariffs or regulations, especially in Europe.

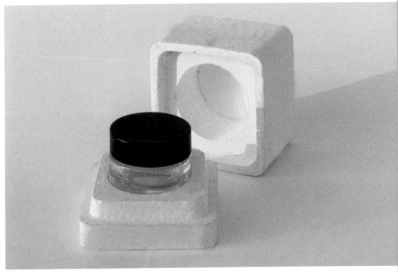

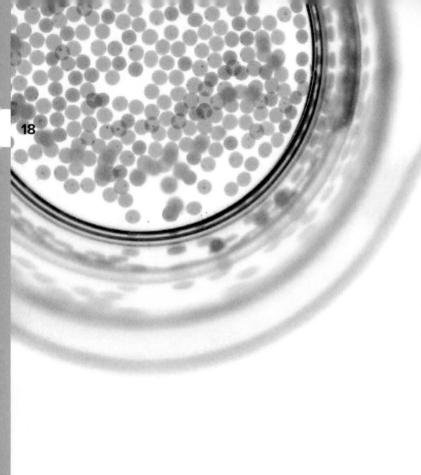

UNIVERSITY PROJECT, UNITED KINGDOM
PLANT plASTIC!

PLANT plASTIC! is a packaging material that doesn't contain any toxic ingredients and that doesn't become waste. Instead, at the end of its use, it takes a new life form by growing into a house plant.

Packaging is not passive dead matter anymore, it's alive and contributes to a better environment. By growing into a plant, more CO_2 is absorbed from the air, and single-use packaging consumption is reduced as the user will grow fresh products such as tomatoes that are normally sold wrapped in plastic. PLANT plASTIC! is made of sodium alginate, Azospirillum Brasilense and plant seeds. Azospirillum Brasilense is a soil bacteria that's harmless to humans, and, because of its nitrogen-fixing property, it promotes plant growth. For this reason, this bacteria is well known as biofertilizer. In her initial experiments, Cinzia made PLANT plASTIC! in the form of beads. The preparation of alginate beads containing bacteria and seeds is fairly easy, and, at the end of the process, preferred shapes can be achieved through molds. The result is then dried, so the bacteria will be inactive but alive, and it will become active again only when it is planted into the soil. For this reason, Azospirillum Brasilense won't contaminate any products in the packaging.

"I believe that in terms of design efficiency we should pay closer attention to nature. We need lightness in materials which not only means less matter but more efficiency: products need to sense and respond to changes in the environment."

BRONZE AWARD WINNER
Cinzia Ferrari,
Biodesigner, United Kingdom

Inspired by group work undertaken during the MA Biodesign at Central Saint Martins in collaboration with Emily Roscoe, Meiqi Peng, Moises Hernandez, and Paula Camiña,

All images are MA Biodesign projects done by the group in the Grow Lab, Central Saint Martins UAL. Tutors: Nancy Diniz, Alice Taylor, Shem Johnson.

Coffee Talk with Cinzia

Two questions, Cinzia: Who are you and what do you do? I am a multidisciplinary designer based in London. I graduated from Politecnico di Milano and now I'm doing a master's in Biodesign at Central Saint Martins, where I undertake research at the intersection between design and biology for sustainable innovation.

How did your journey towards sustainability begin? It was a gradual process, but there is a particular experience that left a mark on me. A few years ago I was in Fiji working on Marine Biology research on shark behavior and ecosystem balance. This contact with nature and the observation of the delicate environmental balance sparked something in me.

Now Cinzia, tell us about PLANT plASTIC. It is a packaging material that doesn't become waste, but instead it grows into a houseplant. These days terms such as biodegradable, compostable, recyclable are everywhere, but they're not very well defined and explained. Biodegradable in industrial terms does not mean that you can just bury it in the garden. I decided I wanted to make a material that is truly easy to biodegrade and yes, you can plant it in your garden.

What have been the biggest challenges? What I struggled with during my project was to find the right mix of disciplines that is manageable for me with my background that is not chemistry, physics or microbiology. I always look for advice and collaborations from experts, and this also adds more value and fun to the project. It's also difficult to find funding, because Biodesign is a very new field and it's very specific.

What can we do to fight against plastic pollution in general? One thing that we can do is to be more educated and learn to be better sustainability educators. There is too much confusion in all the terminology and sometimes it's also a little bit greenwashed. And I think that interdisciplinary projects are important because everyone working in different fields as biology, chemistry, material science, or design has a different approach and different ideas, and mixing all of those really creates something new.

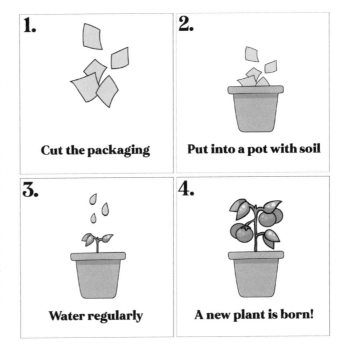

1. Cut the packaging

2. Put into a pot with soil

3. Water regularly

4. A new plant is born!

BIOMATERIALS:
A New Cultural Statement

LABVA is an independent, self-organized community group. Together they create new biomaterials by developing kitchen recipes or growing them. Learn more about the LABVA team and their initiative on page 120.

LTR: Alejandro Weiss, Valentina Aliaga, Esteban Osses, Gabriela Carrasco and María José Besoain

TOP 20

UNIVERSITY PROJECT, ITALY

Peel Saver – Ecological Fries Packaging

Italian designers Pietro Gaeli, Simone Caronni, and Paolo Stefano Gentile came up with a brilliant idea for a project in their course "sustainable design/materials & technologies" led by professor Barbara Pollini at the Nuova Accademia di Belle Arti in Milano, Italy.

Fries companies produce a lot of potato peels as waste. Why not use the peels to create a cool and eco-friendly street food packaging which replaces plasticized paper packaging? Potato peels consist of starches and fiber components. After maceration and natural drying, it is an ideal street food packaging material. Nothing has to be added. This way it can be re-inserted in the biological cycle as animal food or fertilizer for plants.

Peel Saver is a natural and aesthetic way to present the food: The fries are served in the same peel that originally protected the potato. The Motto: Return to simplicity and use what nature already designed for us!

Pietro Gaeli, Simone Caronni, Paolo Stefano Gentile, University Project, Italy

MARIA MAYER, GERMANY
Algae Pattern

The use of colored dyes in textile production and the fast fashion system are difficult environmental issues. For Maria Mayer as a textile designer, it is impossible to imagine working without color. It is therefore of great importance for her to try new ways of experimenting with color in fashion and interior design. In order to preserve the water that has already been dyed, she has developed a process in which this colored water is mixed with algae powder as an ingredient to produce a printing paste without polluting the environment, thus creating patterns on the textiles.

In a circular design process, the already dyed water and algae mix is stirred into a printable paste by adding heat. This paste can then be applied to the textiles in existing textile printing processes like screen printing, stamp coloring, and mold casting on fabric. Patterns up to the 3D level can also be created. Maria sees the addition of algae as a binding agent for an organic, future-oriented ingredient that can help reduce the tons of contamination from microplastics and toxins. Among the algae, some species are heat resistant up to 90 °C and are thus suitable as a textile binding agent due to their hardy properties.

In order to compliment the raw dyes created from nature, the printing paste is made from old dye baths which are also made from natural raw materials. To show the three basic colors, the printing paste is made from extracts of turmeric cochineal and jasmine flowers.

TOP 20

Maria Mayer,
Textile Designer, Germany

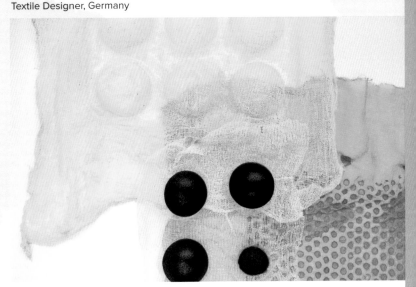

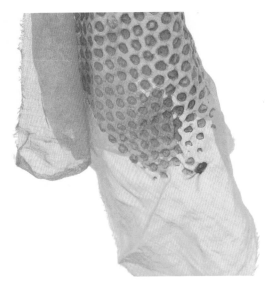

TOP 20

MALU LÜCKING, GERMANY

Cladophora – A Water Saving Resource

Because of its wasteful use of material and water resources, the textile industry is one of the main factors contributing to the ecological imbalance of fresh water and saltwater systems. But now part of this water crisis becomes part of its solution: Cladophora is a filamentous alga growing in abundance because of human activity. This project harvests the fibrous algae from Berlin lakes and utilizes their different qualities to produce textiles.

Cladophora can be processed into translucent, non-woven fabric or to be woven as yarn into a surface. With other biodegradable additives, it can also be processed into a compostable bioplastic which could, in the future, replace PVC foil for raincoats or bags in the fast fashion industry.

Malu Lücking,
Designer, Germany

CARETWICE, GERMANY

CareTwice

Did you know that when you buy conventional shampoo, you're buying a plastic bottle filled with at least 80 % water? Not so with the CareTwice powder shampoo! The powder comes in paper sachets that you can use directly or dissolve in water and store in a reusable bottle at home. Powder shampoo is also convenient and lightweight for travel.

The all-female start-up CareTwice wants to solve the global plastic problem by removing the need for single-use plastic in soap and shampoo bottles. The founders take great care in using only natural and vegan ingredients without micro-plastics – making it the ideal sustainable and high-quality shampoo for caring twice: For you and the environment.

Lena Scholpp, Inken Barz, Hailey Gahlon, Carina Kaiser, CareTwice, Germany

elieve **that people can care ut themselves and the ironment at the same time.**

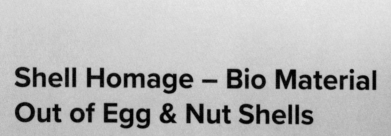

Shell Homage – Bio Material Out of Egg & Nut Shells

Shell Homage is a biodegradable composite material out of egg and nut shells. The surface looks like marble or natural stone and is handcrafted into a unique combination of colors and patterns. Learn more about Rania Elkalla's beautiful material on page 82.

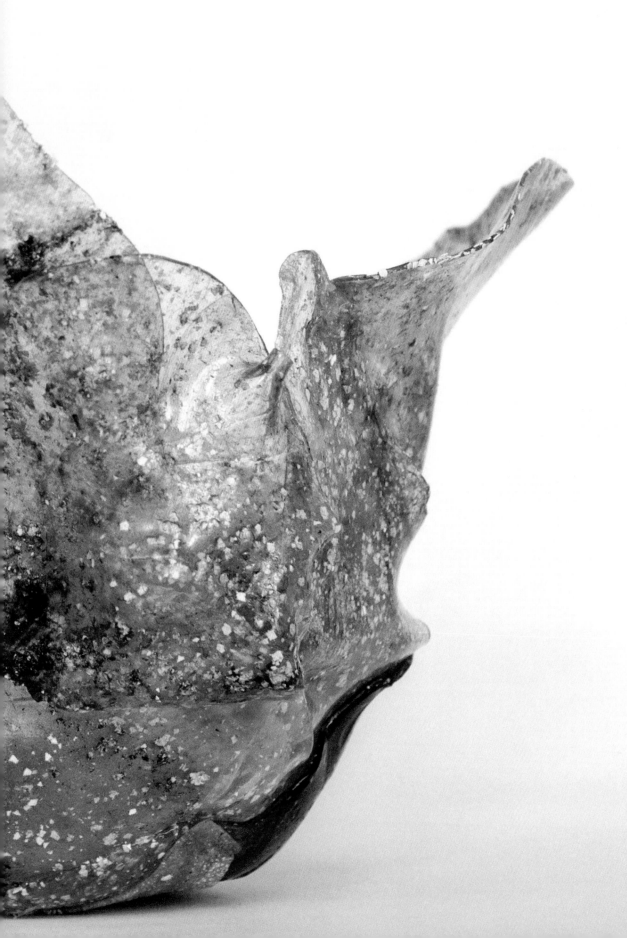

27

NÚRIA VILA, SPAIN

Compostable Packaging & Coffee Ink

Slowmov is a coffee bar located in Barcelona, which works with specialty coffee only. They contribute with a quality alternative that respects the environment and gives value to the slow process. Designer Núria Vila was commissioned to design a compostable packaging.

Slowmov sourced a bag from a Canadian brand called TekPack Solutions that can biodegrade in 180 days, the same rate as the skin of an orange. Núria created a coffee ink from used coffee grounds to be manually and locally screenprinted on each of the coffee bags. This allows Slowmov to customize and make a limited series of bags. To add information on each coffee bag, a solvent-free recycled paper label from the German brand Memo "Recycling Plus" was used.

In addition to the packaging, Slowmov wanted to give their wholesale customers postcards with information about their coffee. For this purpose, they used paper made from recycled paper cups from the English brand Extract from G.F Smith. The color paper is the chromatic color that is used in another packaging that identifies the origin of coffee beans.

Núria Vila
Silk-screen Printing: @coyoteatelier
Illustration: @naimonpaper
Customer: @slowmov,
Designer, Spain

VALDÍS STEINARSDÓTTIR, ICELAND

Bioplastic Skin

Bioplastic Skin is a biodegradable packaging for meat made out of the skin of the animal itself. Animal hides are often considered to be a useless by-product in the meat industry. If we choose to consume meat, it is our responsibility to utilize the whole animal and to do it with as little pollution to our planet as possible. As consumers, we have become so detached from the origins of our food. We're now used to the perfectly cut, plastic-wrapped products that are offered to us in stores.

The Bioplastic Skin project also addresses the problem of the excessive use of plastic that has become widespread and commonplace in food packaging. Every day huge quantities of plastic packaging are thrown away that eventually end up in landfills or the ocean. This project aims to reduce the use of plastic in the food industry, in particular, the meat industry. Meat consumption and the use of excessive plastic are reaching a critical point and it is clear that we as a society need to rethink our consumeristic pattern.

Valdís Steinarsdóttir,
Designer, Iceland

Camilo Cerro,
Dharmatecture, United Arab Emirates

DHARMATECTURE, UNITED ARAB EMIRATES

Urban Acupuncture: Producing Water in Informal Settlements

The plastic pollution problem is directly linked with the growing urbanization and the derived ecological challenges as supplying clean water. According to the United Nations, the global number of urban inhabitants is estimated to grow from around four billion to over six billion people by 2050. The majority of this increasing population is expected to live in informal settlements, where the inhabitants will have to deal with inadequate or non-existent water, health or sanitation systems.

Camilo Cerro conceived a concept which he calls Urban Acupuncture, by which only small-scale interventions are required to produce large-scale social change. The idea is the following: At any given time, there are three quadrillion gallons of water in the atmosphere, which, if a minimal fraction of it gets tapped, could solve water scarcity. The annual average humidity of cities like Karachi in Pakistan or Mumbai in India is around 70%. This makes them ideal sites for the use of atmospheric water generators, as these devices are designed to produce water from humidity levels as low as 35%. A single atmospheric water generator can produce up to 5,000 liters of clean, filtered water per day. Functioning as a hive, these water towers would be placed at multiple social nodes within an informal settlement. This could potentially solve the water crisis by producing clean, filtered, free, accessible water – and by doing so eliminating health and sanitation issues.

KAWAMURA LAB, JAPAN

Coffee Grounds As Wood Substitute in Producing Cellulose

Every year, six million tons of coffee grounds are produced globally as solid residues after brewing coffee. A major part of spent coffee grounds is simply discarded without any recycling or burned as fuel in the coffee industry. Professor Izuru Kawamura and his research group at Yokohama National University revealed that cell walls account for approximately 50% of the dry weight of coffee grounds. For this reason, they developed an upcycling concept that isolates cellulose nanofibers from coffee grounds. Their long-term aim is to develop a value-added product from waste coffee grounds in an environmentally-friendly manner.

Izuru Kawamura, Noriko Kanai
Kawamura Lab, Yokohama National University, Japan

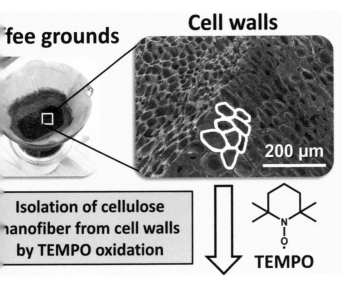

Cell walls

fee grounds

200 µm

Isolation of cellulose nanofiber from cell walls by TEMPO oxidation

TEMPO

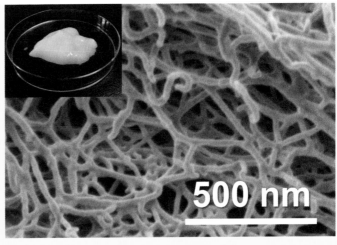

500 nm

Cellulose nanofibers

JOHANNES BAUER, GERMANY
Starch and Fibres – Material Studies

Johannes Bauer,
Product Designer, Germany

Johannes' project began at an exhibition about Christien Meindertsma at the Vitra Design Museum, where her FLAX CHAIR was shown. He was very impressed by the project at the time, and sometime later, he started working with the same material PLA which is often referred to as bioplastic. During his research, he invetigated that this material also has some problems in terms of sustainability. So why use PLA as a material at all? Why not just use a natural material?

This project is therefore dedicated on the one hand to finding an alternative material with properties similar to those of plastic, but with chemically unchanged ingredients – i.e. biodegradable and without negative effects on our environment. On the other hand, to be able to grow and produce our own 'plastic' at home.

In order to produce a material with similar properties to plastic, potato starch is mixed with flax fibers. Since this compound material is still water-soluble, it must be sealed with a layer of natural resin. Before sealing, the material can also be sanded and polished to a high gloss.

STEVEN AKOUN, FRANCE

Foamation. Acoustic Tiles From Recycled Glass and Egg Shell

Designer Steven Akoun researched the possible uses and visual potential of glass foam in a laboratory in Rennes, France. He found that one of the most obvious properties of the material was its impressive sound insulation capabilities. In fact, noise pollution is an important health issue today. Thanks to their porous aspect, these wall tiles absorb sound waves very efficiently.

They are a visually striking alternative to polymer-based foams and are made with recycled glass bottles and reclaimed egg shells. The tiles are suitable for use in noisy indoor areas such as workplaces and restaurants. While in Amsterdam for a design residency, Steven was inspired by the city's diverse and vivid brick paving for the shapes and patterns that he designed. The project is an ongoing study around sound efficiency, color and motif combinations as well as sustainability.

Steven Akoun,
Designer, France

Desintegra.me

Learn more about Margarita Talep's beautiful material that uses pigments extracted from the skin of discarded fruit and vegetables on page 86.

Marta Galiazzo, Michele Stignani,
Gianmarco Giacometti, Erika Moriconi,
WAO, Italy

WAO, ITALY

WAO – The Eco Effect Shoes

With their experience in the fashion industry, the team at WAO knows how much fashion contributes to environmental pollution. They wanted to create a product that safeguards our beautiful planet, so they have designed entirely ecological sneakers made with sustainable and natural materials. These sneakers can be disposed of at the end of their lives through innovative processes like vermiculture.

The Italian designers at WAO have created a hemp sneaker model that requires 75 % less water than cotton to grow, with no pesticides needed, and dyed only with vegetal dyes. Additionally, they have designed a water-resistant model made with 100 % regenerated nylon. Both models have natural degradable soles and natural insoles where no chemical glue is used.

The shoes are made in Italy and WAO works in a transparent supply chain specifically with companies sensitive to steer clear of environmental pollution and to foster social sustainability.

FORMCARD, UNITED KINGDOM

Melt, Mold, Make, Mend

Formcard is the brainchild of British Artist and Designer Peter Marigold. It is a pocket-sized card of meltable bioplastic that you can use to make, fix and modify the world around you. Just drop it in a cup of hot water and then you can mold it quickly to make little solutions to everyday problems. By simply reheating it you can reuse it again and again.

Yes, Formcard is plastic, but it is a starch-based biodegradable plastic, and it can be used to fix and reuse broken plastic products to extend their lifespan. Peter Marigold runs creative workshops where you can explore the potential of Formcard's applications, and he also uses this versatile material in his artistic work.

Peter Marigold,
FORMcard, United Kingdom

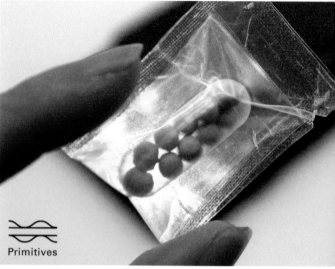

Primitives

PRIMITIVES BIODESIGN, UNITED STATES

Compostable, Biomimetic Films

Noa Machover, Viirj Kan, Rebecca Wilson,
Primitives Biodesign, United States

Primitives is an early-stage biomaterials start-up that is comprised of an all technical and all-female team with backgrounds in biopolymers, smart materials, and sustainable design. It engineers 'smart', compostable, and bio-based plastic film alternatives that respond to environmental stimuli, exhibit property-change, and biodegrade after use.

Primitives has engineered high-performance, multi-layered films that are compostable, safe, and even edible. These films are made from 100 % bio-based, renewable materials. The films can be integrated into a range of applications. Imagine: Guilt-free snack packaging to bury in your planter after use. Insulin labels that respond to extreme temperatures, letting you know when it's no longer safe. Supplement packaging that changes color when it's been punctured. Meat wraps that reveal when the contents are spoiled. Milk that tells you it's gone bad.

Primitives incorporates mechanisms that are inspired by stimuli-responsive systems in nature, such as pine cones that change shape, flowers that emit smells, and chameleon skins that shift colors.

Plasis – A Plastic-Eating Fungi

Plasis is a Mexican University project which aims to rid the world of plastic. The researchers behind the project didn't just want to move trash from point A to point B by recycling, they looked further into biotechnology. They saw that fungi can make wonderful things, from great medicine to consumer products and materials such as semi-leather. One of the amazing characteristics of fungi is their capability to eat hydrocarbons, which suggests the possibility that they can eat plastic, too. Multiple studies have been undertaken to investigate these theories.

The team started their experiments with the mentorship at the University of Monterrey's Microbiology Lab and saw promising results. Right now, they are continuing to improve the process and eventually aim to create working products.

39

Daniela Fernandez, Alejandra Diaz Lozano, David Enrique Sada Moreno, With the mentorship of the University of Monterrey´s Microbiology Lab, University Project, Mexico

Go Green. Go Wild.

This is the stylish and reusable deodorant from Wild that utilizes the powers of the natural world to create an effective, long-lasting deodorant. Learn more about the beautiful product on page 97.

Elin Tornblad – CEO & Co-Founder,
Pontus Törnqvist – Inventor & Co-Founder,
Potato Plastic, Sweden

POTATO PLASTIC, SWEDEN

Potato Plastic

Potato Plastic is a plastic-like material that is totally bio-degradable and made only from unharmful and natural ingredients. The material is suitable for single-use items like cutlery, bags, and straws. It all started as an accident in Pontus Törnqvist's student kitchen in Lund in 2018. When trying to create plastic from algae for a school project, Pontus tried to use potato starch as a binder. Some of it escaped to the floor and was discovered two days later – and the rest is, as you say, history.

Since then, the material has been developed further by Pontus at a food lab in Copenhagen, as well as in Gothenburg. The idea was matched with a team of entrepreneurs at Chalmers School of Entrepreneurship where it was transformed into a real company.

HOLLY GROUNDS, UNITED KINGDOM
Dissolvable Noodle Packaging

In the current world of instant ramen noodles, there is often more plastic than noodles. With 100 billion annual servings worldwide, instant noodles can be cooked and eaten in under ten minutes. The plastic packaging, however, can take eight decades or more to decompose. Most curbside recycling schemes do not accept plastic film packaging, contributing considerably to plastic pollution. This devastating issue encouraged Product Designer Holly Grounds to develop a solution during her second year studying Product Design at Ravensbourne University London. The result? The dissolvable noodle pack.

Dry noodles are packaged in an edible, tasteless starch-based film that dissolves in contact with boiling water. To eliminate plastic sachets of seasonings, the dried spices and flavorings have been incorporated into the starch-based film at the manufacturing stage. When cooked, the film dissolves and the seasonings are released into the noodles without the need for fiddly plastic sachets. The bio-based film is heat-sealed to ensure the noodles stay fresh. The noodle parcels are packaged in a wax-coated paper outer layer for hygiene purposes and to further reduce plastic use.

Holly Grounds,
Product Designer, United Kingdom

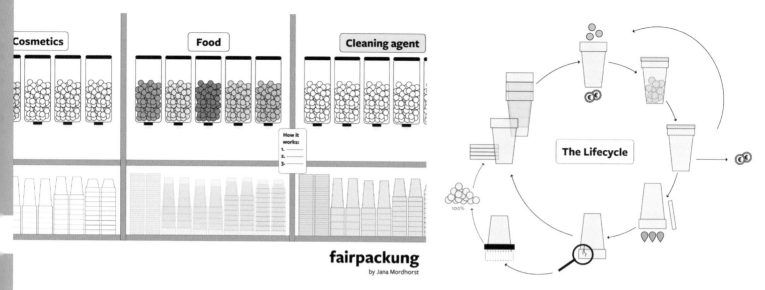

FAIRPACKUNG, GERMANY
Fairpackung

Fairpackung makes Zero Waste Shopping more accessible. To buy unpacked food, often extensive planning is required to bring your own containers, which can be an inconvenience when you are on the go. Fairpackung solves this problem. It is a circular deposit system with robust, lightweight, and easy to transport containers, which can be borrowed at the store. There are three container categories: food, cleaning agent, and cosmetics – the customer chooses the size. This concept makes spontaneous shopping in bulk possible. Moreover, it's a great way to reach new target groups who are not yet participating in Zero Waste Shopping.

Currently, Jana Mordhorst, the inventor of Fairpackung, is planning to use bio-based plastic from responsible sources. The long-term goal is to use bioplastic, which has a positive CO_2 footprint. The trend of buying unpacked products will grow over the next years and so it will also be of utmost importance to include health food stores and supermarkets into this reuse, deposit and return cycle, too.

Jana Mordhorst,
Fairpackung, Germany

Strano Microfactory

Strano is a sustainable microfactory which supplies bio-materials for designers, artists, and every creative person who chooses a new way to produce, consume, and have the courage to believe in this new path. Strano's bio-material can adopt any shape, can be rigid or soft, it can be laser cut and engraved, and also sewed and knitted.

Strano Microfactory supports their customers' creative process, designing the material together based on their requirements, defining all the variants: color, thickness, texture, flexibility. Strano was born to bring people closer to sustainable alternatives, to empower them by offering biomaterials, and to create together a better world.

Lucrecia Strano, Anastasia Pistofidou, Betiana Pavon, Ana Correa, Strano Microfactory, Spain

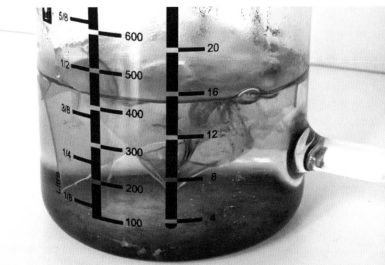

MOST PRACTICAL SOLUTIONS

In this category, we present solutions for a world with less plastic which are pragmatic, effective, clear & simple, useful, practicable, constructive, viable, functional, rational, no-nonsense, applicable, nuts & bolts, both feet on the ground, commonsensical, straightforward, user-oriented and purposeful.

48

79

PONTO BIODESIGN, BRAZIL
Unpack Less, Peel More

Following circular design guidelines, Ponto Biodesign aims to create a packaging that enables the materials to flow in integrated and regenerative loops. The packaging system was created for handmade personal care products, manufactured locally with natural ingredients. The project consists of a collection of five different packages. Each of them has three layers: the internal layer is the creamy personal care product – such as face cream, deodorant, facial clay, etc. The second layer is made of solid natural soap and it serves as a container for the previous layer. Finally, the external layer – as well as the tags and strings – is made out of bacterial cellulose, that can simply be glued together with water, protects the soap, and contains the information of the product. The packaging system reproduces the structure of a fruit, juice – pulp – peel. The material for the external layer was developed using experimental processes of biofabrication with residual SCOBYs from local Kombucha producers. It is fully compostable, made from renewable sources, and has a fast growth rate. Being local, it eliminates the need to transport raw materials from long distances and increases the integration of local initiatives.

Natural pigments like spirulina, hibiscus, saffron, and charcoal were added to the blending process, giving different colors and properties to the samples. The manufacturing process has a low level of energy consumption and is a low-tech process. It can be made regionally generating local jobs and facilitates the control of a fair and safe working environment in the production line.

GOLD AWARD WINNER
Elena Amato, Caroline Pagnan,
Designer, Ponto Biodesign,
Universidade do Estado de Minas Gerais, Brazil

Coffee Talk with Elena

Please tell us who you are and what you do. My name is Elena Amato. I am a product designer from Guatemala, but right now I live in Brazil, studying for my master's degree in Design Materials and Sustainability. I'm the founder of Ponto Biodesign, a biomaterial experimental lab, where I develop materials from bacterial cellulose and food waste.

First, I made packaging for cosmetics as part of my graduation project with the aim to design a more sustainable packaging system for handmade cosmetics with natural ingredients. I researched about edible packaging designs and I thought that if there's food packaging made out of food, we could have cosmetic packaging made out of soap, too. After that, I decided to research bacterial cellulose in order to develop a protective layer for it.

I've started to collaborate with companies to develop materials from their waste. Because I don't have a manufacturing process ready to scale, we experiment and make concepts that we could make for the future.

What are the biggest challenges you face? One of the biggest obstacles I find is that people compare these new materials with existing ones, especially when we talk about their costs. We are so used to having and buying a lot of things and paying almost nothing for them. It's a big obstacle to get people to understand that we are paying so little, probably because someone in the production chain didn't get a fair payment or because our environment was harmed in some way. At some point, we're going to have to financially, socially, and environmentally pay for the damage that we have caused with our unsustainable consumption.

What do you think we all can do to solve the plastic pollution problem in general? We should start by consciously analyzing the consequences of our actions on a daily basis with small things, like trying to be thoughtful when choosing what we buy and just thinking about the wider context. We should always be asking ourselves; who, how, and where the objects that surround us were made? Where does our waste go? Is there an alternative that avoids waste? What are the objects made of? Are those materials good for us and the environment? What are the impacts of the choices we've made regarding what we eat or how that food is prepared? The more we ask ourselves those kinds of questions, the more it will become natural to make better choices.

For me, we have to start by talking about it. In order to get people to care about it, they have to know they have to do something.

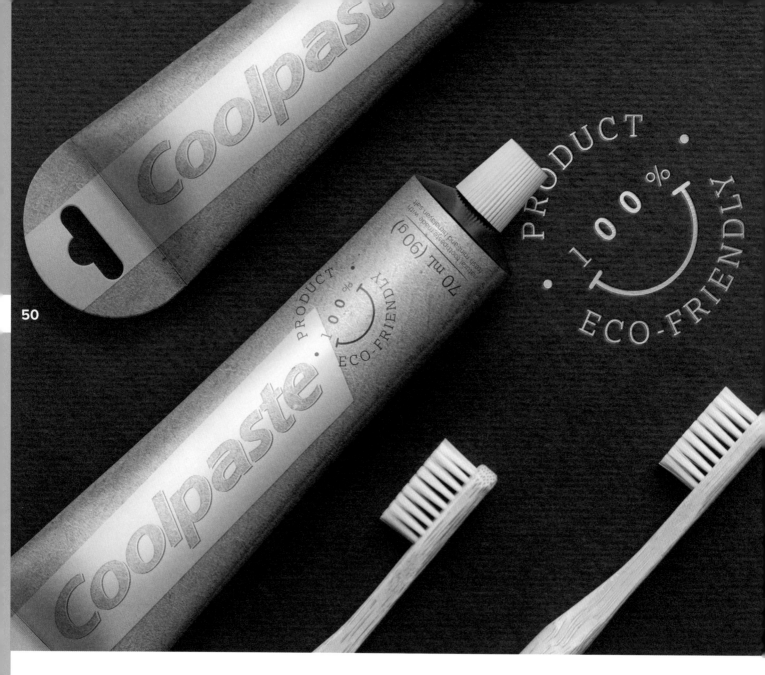

50

ALLAN GOMES, BRAZIL

Coolpaste – Think Outside the Box!

Coolpaste is a sustainable packaging design that literally thinks outside the box. The concept started with the desire to solve a problem for one of the most popular everyday products and the first step to our mornings, toothpaste. The aim was to develop an eco-responsible packaging design for toothpaste in a way that didn't affect its durability while being transported or stacked on shelves. After an in-depth point-of-sale study about the Colgate brand, it was noted that the paper box could be eliminated without affecting the integrity of the toothpaste. In the final proposal, Coolpaste was presented as a product that would

hang instead of being stacked. By reducing waste and offering a new disposal for this product category, it became lighter. Also, instead of using the conventional plastic tube, Coolpaste uses impermeable cardboard – similar to the material used by the food industry. The cap of the tube is also biodegradable, made from Polylactide (PLA), a bioplastic derived from renewable resources, such as corn starch, tapioca roots, potato starch, or sugarcane. This design solves logistical and environmental issues for global toothpaste brands if implemented.

Coffee Talk with Allan

Please tell us a bit about yourself, Allan! Well, I'm a curious and ambitious Brazilian packaging designer, now based in Toronto, where I am pursuing my master's degree at York University. My involvement with design started early in my life. In 2005, when I was 15 years old, my father opened a print shop, and I supported this family business by creating graphic arts for new clients. Then I joined the design program at the Federal University of Minas Gerais. Since then, I've been fascinated by packaging design, and I spent five years working as a senior designer in a creative agency specialized in branding and packaging design. Now, I work as a freelancer allowing me to manage my time whilst I'm doing my master's studies.

What motivated you to get into sustainability? In our consumer world, graphic design is often limited as a means to make brands sell more products. This always bothered me because my motivation for sustainability comes from the desire to use all the knowledge to promote the good. Personally, the trigger for acting and thinking sustainably was my experience with a shamanic medicine from the Amazon Rainforest, the Ayahuasca, which is a plant-based tea with a powerful capacity to make us connect with nature. This inner experience changed the way I see my role as a designer and citizen in this world.

How did you come up with Coolpaste? Our packaging design professor at the university in Brazil challenged us to develop a new packaging concept for an existing product. I chose to work with toothpaste because it's a mass-produced item presenting our daily lives with single-use packaging causing a substantial environmental impact. The initial proposal was to remove the paper box and make the tube possible to be hanged at point-of-sale. The idea of replacing the material of the tube from plastic to laminated paper came up years later.

What is a possible future for Coolpaste? Coolpaste had fantastic visibility on the Internet, and I got in contact with many oral care companies, including Colgate. But most of the companies wanted to see proof that my prototype would work in practice. Fortunately, I now have a solid collaboration with an industrial partner in Brazil, and they are making all the material tests and production preparations. So, it's becoming a reality now.

What do you think can we do on a large scale to fight against plastic pollution? Well, this is a tough question. It's a structural problem, and it will take time to solve. Some scientific innovations may arise to alleviate the crisis, especially when it comes to plastic from renewable sources. But I personally think that the only way to fight this crisis is to focus on the education and awareness of our society formed by a mass of critical consumers. As consumers, we have the potential power to ask for change. The most effective act of protest within our capitalist system is refusing to consume the wrong products.

51

SILVER AWARD WINNER
Allan Gomes,
Designer, Coolpaste, Brazil

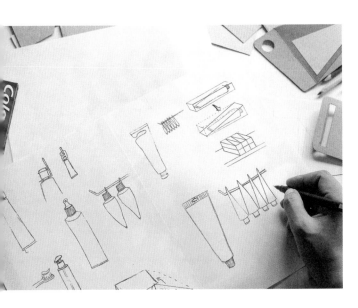

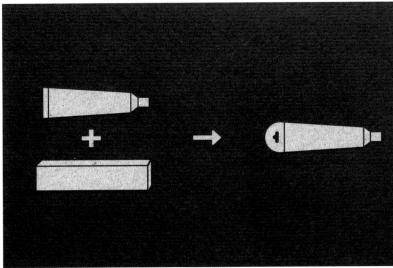

ECOSOC, SOMALIA
Building the World

ECOSOC is a social enterprise based in Mogadishu, Somalia, spearheaded by a team of young environmentalists who have a background in Medicine and Environmental Conservation. In order to clean up the cities from plastic waste, they have introduced an innovative, chemical-free, and energy-conserving plastic extrusion technology called "Waxy ɪɪ" to recycle and to transform post-consumer plastic waste, packaging materials, and agricultural waste into durable and environmentally friendly roof tiles, interlocking bricks, paving stones and deck beams. This reduces the need for building material manufactured from wood, helping to preserve the environment and forests, prevent deforestation, and thus mitigating climate change.

The passionate team collects waste from households, businesses, and municipal markets and takes it to decentralized sorting sites where it gets sorted into more than 40 fractions. It is then composted from organic waste into high-quality compost. Other waste materials as paper, glass, and metal are also recycled. The cities are divided into different zones, where ECOSOC engages youth and women groups to facilitate the collection and delivery of plastics to the sorting sites. The beauty of the recycled products: They are durable, cost-effective, aesthetic, insect resistant, and easy to work with. The young bright minds of this social enterprise have an ambitious three-year strategic plan: 1. Recycle over 2.5 million kg of plastic and save an estimated 250 acres of forest. 2. Prevent 2,500 tons of carbon dioxide gas emissions. 3. Create 300 direct jobs.

BRONZE AWARD WINNER
Mohamed Hassan Mahamad, Dr. Mohamed Abdirashid Farah, Shamso Hus
ECOSOC, Somalia

Coffee Talk with Mohamed Hassan

Who are you and what do you do? My name is Mohamed Hassan. I am the founder of ECOSOC Somalia. Plastics are often portrayed as a culprit of environmental degradation, but it doesn't have to be that way. ECOSOC is a social enterprise that addresses the challenges of urban waste management including plastic pollution, chronic youth unemployment, deforestation, and climate change. We collect waste plastic and manufacture eco-friendly roof tiles, interlocking bricks, and deck beams from it. We employ a reliably working technology, local labor, and resources to produce innovative products and help solve pressing socio-economic and environmental challenges.

What motivated you to get into sustainability? This was a gradual process. I have lived both in the coastal towns of Mogadishu and Kismayu. I have seen what plastic pollution has done to the marine ecosystem. I have left active employment to pursue this mission. The mission of cleaning Somalia's coastline and making a living out of it for others.

How did you come up with your project idea? I started reading documents and consulting like-minded people on how to clean up the waste. I wanted to come up with a social project that cleans the environment as well as creates employment.

What is a possible future for ECOSOC? My plan is to expand this project into other coastal towns. Somalia has the longest coastline in Africa but all locations have the same problem of plastic waste. It would be a joy to see our concept implemented in all the coastal towns of Somalia.

What do you see as the biggest obstacles on your way? Insecurity and lack of financial funds. Instability in Somalia has made it difficult for environmental activists to work in peace. Remnants of explosives are also left behind in waste and hence can cause explosions and deaths during collection. Due to the volatile nature of the region, it is also difficult to get financial funding.

What do you think will be the solution to the plastic pollution problem on a large scale? Creating alternatives for plastics. Plastics should be avoided at all costs. Man has prospered long before the advent of plastics. Big Multinationals that deal with plastics must be put to task to account for their plastic generation. Social enterprises that are engaged in plastic collection and recycling must be helped financially and technically to enable them to run effectively.

Aqua Faba Foam

The material of these bowls is based on aquafaba from chickpeas and shows great potential for mechanical manufacturing and thus for industrial production. Learn more about Paula Nerlich's beautiful material on page 84.

Alexander Cuellar Osorio, Sonia Mendez Cristancho
Green Pack SAS, Colombia

GREEN PACK SAS, COLOMBIA

Biodegradable Food Packaging

GREENPACK is a Colombian company dedicated to the design and manufacturing of biodegradable, compostable, recyclable, and sustainable packaging.

The team recently developed a new composite packaging material using two types of biopolymers by extruding biodegradable waste. Ecovio is a biopolymer extracted directly from starch of organic residues and PLA (Polylactic Acid) gets extracted from corn starch. The engineering team designed a tri-layer packaging for coffee grounds and beans using a substrate of Ecovio, a layer of PLA sugar cane paper composition, and an aluminum sprinkling coating.

The packaging meets the requirements of the Colombian legislation of packaging to come into contact with food, by providing barriers to lighting, humidity, and gases.

To calculate the total sum of heavy metals, a migration analysis was conducted which showed favorable results. Only 0.375 mg/kg, where the allowable limit is up to 100 mg/kg and an average total migration of simulants of only 2.02 mg/kg also far below the allowable maximum limit of 8.0 mg/kg.

These are impressive technical characteristics for a biomaterial that is sourced and manufactured locally with an ecologically responsible footprint.

BAYONIX, GERMANY

A Bottle From Cradle-to-Cradle

The BAYONIX BOTTLE is a solution to fight the plastic waste, microplastic, and pollution problem using the cradle-to-cradle approach of a circular economy.

It was designed and tested to be completely free of pollutants (not just BPA-free) that usually pass from a plastic bottle to the beverage. Thus, there is no unpleasant odor and taste due to the outgassing that occurs with conventional plastics. It is fully recyclable without loss of quality and demonstrably fully biodegradable, leaving no microplastic behind. It is safe for humans, animals, and the environment.

As a sports bottle, it is very practical to use. It is easy to fill, clean, and drink from, it comes without additional, toxic rubber seals and is completely waterproof (really!), and very stable. It has an ergonomic drinking opening with quick release, a snap hook and fits into any standard bottle cage.

What's more, it is manufactured locally where it was invented by Stefan Hunger — in Beautiful Bavaria!

Stefan Hunger
Bayonix, Germany

WALTZ SEVEN GMBH, AUSTRIA

Sustainable Disposable Razor

Thomas Grüner
Waltz Seven GmbH, Austria

The vision of the Vienna-based start-up ecoSHAVE is to create a bathroom without plastic waste thanks to innovative hygiene products and high-tech materials.

ecoSHAVE's mission? To reduce plastic waste when shaving — for the first clean shave.

Globally, we use around 5 billion disposable razors every year which end up in household waste. This means up to 100,000 tons of different types of plastic are manufactured, processed, and finally burned or trashed. ecoSHAVE wants to change this. They've created the first sustainable, disposable razor that saves up to 75% plastic compared to standard disposable razors.

The founders have succeeded in finding a high-tech substance that replaces a large part of the plastic with wood residues from sustainable forestry. The wood fibers come from certified, renewable wood stocks in Scandinavia and are a by-product of paper production. The use of sustainable wood fibers firstly saves plastic in production and secondly reduces CO_2 emissions. The premium razor blades are made using Swedish steel to ensure a high-quality shave.

The product is not 100% plastic-free today, but it uses much less plastic than other disposable razors. ecoSHAVE's goal is to remove 100% of the plastic element within two years, thus saving thousands of tons of plastic every year.

NIUWAY AG, SWITZERLAND
Sustainable Festival Tent

The Swiss start-up company Niuway AG has developed a high-quality and durable tent made from two recyclable materials (PET and Aluminum) to provide a solution for the rampant tent waste at major events and festivals. The Niuway tent fulfills all the criteria for a leisure tent but is optimized for use at outdoor music festivals and big outdoor events. Typically tents at such events are only used once and are disposed of afterward – resulting in a lot of waste. In addition, such tents are made from a variety of materials. For this reason, recycling is not possible.

Based on this, the founders created a tent that consists solely of two recyclable materials (PET and aluminum) and designed it in such a way that both materials can be easily separated. Although PET is a conventional plastic material that carries the associated ecological problems, Niuway has developed a recycling process to ensure the material of both the fabric and the poles can return into the material cycle. Consumers can also use the tent several times, so it has a long product lifecycle.

Florian Felder,
Niuway AG, Switzerland

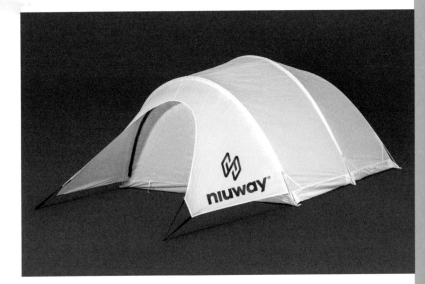

Bioplastic Skin

Contents and packaging are derived from the same source; packaging for meat made out of the skin of the animal itself. Learn more about Valdís Steinarsdóttir's innovative material on page 29.

*Packaging should behave
just like an orange peel,
so nature won't even notice
we're here.*

PLACE THIS IN THE COMPOST

Rebecca Najjar-Rudick, Daphna Nissenbaum,
CEO & Co-Founder of TIPA, Israel

TIPA, ISRAEL

Back to Basics.
Back to Earth.

TIPA is a developer and producer of fully compostable flexible packaging that breaks down into compost just like organic material. The Israeli company was founded in 2010 by Daphna Nissenbaum and Tal Neuman to address the plastic waste challenge.

Inspired by nature's perfect packaging, TIPA created a ground-breaking material that undergoes the same biodegradation process as organic waste, just like an orange peel or walnut shells. TIPA replaces conventional flexible plastic with fully compostable packaging so that plastic will no longer linger in landfills for hundreds of years, but instead will biodegrade within months in a sustainable end-of-life process.

The goal was to achieve a circular economy through a true recycling process of composting. The team at TIPA works closely with businesses of all types to design and provide packaging ideal for their specific application, ranging from fresh produce and snacks to magazines and fashion apparel. The packaging solutions are built to fit existing machinery and supply chains.

KIND2, UNITED KINGDOM

Saving the Planet Doesn't Have To Mean Bad Hair

Founded by Sue Campbell in 2019, KIND2 is the story of a brand wanting to make a difference. This British start-up's mission is to show how plastic-free, soap-free, and cruelty-free haircare can be the new normal. In the first half-year of trading, KIND2 has already saved more than 3,000 plastic bottles from being created.

It was the discovery that shampoo contains 80% water that made Sue realize this was a product ready for innovation. Each 80 g bar lasts for 60 to 80 washes, the equivalent of around 3 x 250 ml bottles. It's estimated one person uses approximately 500 plastic shampoo and conditioner bottles over their lifetime. KIND2's products have a positive impact on the environment through their reformulation, which eliminates both water and plastic at the source. Additional benefits include the reduction in energy used for transportation and storage.

KIND2's impact supports the UN Sustainable Development Goals No. 12 'Responsible Consumption and Production' and No. 14 'Life Below Water'.

Besides being plastic-free, the products which are made in the United Kingdom, are vegan and free from sulfates, silicones, and parabens. Instead, they're full of active plant-based extracts to gently treat specific hair needs. The range is unisex and it isn't soap-based, like many on the market, so it actually works in hard water, with no transition period or vinegar rinse required.

TOP 20

Sue Campbell
Kind2, United Kingdom

63

Jonathan Pohlke,
University Project, Germany

JONATHAN POHLKE, GERMANY

Pius

The Raspberry Pi is a small and low-cost single-board computer, developed by the Raspberry Pi Foundation. The charity's goal is to facilitate the knowledge of basic computer science in schools and for everyone. The Raspberry Pi is used all over the world by a large open-source community, and so far more than 30 million units have been sold.

The single-board computer is sold without a case, which has to be bought separately. Almost all of these cases are made out of plastic. These cases are used all over the world, and most of them are produced in Asia. Aside from the production, which is not very eco-friendly, there is a long shipping distance. This is where Pius comes into play! Thanks to the cardboard material and glueless folding technique, the transport is both low-cost and eco-efficient. With a few folds, the owner has a beautiful and functional case for their Raspberry Pi. The single-board computer can be fixed to Pius conveniently with screws and nuts.

The production uses recycled material and it can also be produced and recycled locally. The solid board is very light but still strong. It is resistant against humidity and it is non-flammable up to 200 °C. Last but not least, the material can be printed individually, meaning that many designs are possible. These properties make the material a perfect new home for the Raspberry Pi. The strong cardboard will last for at least five years under normal circumstances, and after that, you can put it into the paper waste recycling, which has proven to be efficient for many years.

ECO FOR LIFE, UNITED KINGDOM
100 % From Plants

Eco For Life Bottles were born in 2016. After one of the founders discovered a bottle made from plant substances on a trip to Asia, he was so taken with it, that he immediately started to research the material used and how such a bottle could be produced.

Eco For Life Bottles are made from PLA (Polylactic acid), a bio-raw material derived from sugar-based crops, a renewable natural resource.

PLA bottles are helping to make a change for the better. Traditional PET plastic bottles never go truly 'away'. They can only be burnt (the energy industry calls this thermal recovery), dumped in landfill or the sea or be down-cycled to products of a lesser quality. PLA has better end-of-life options.

Michael Shore, Jan Adams,
Tai Ning Grayson, Zoë Shore,
Eco for Life, United Kingdom

The British start-up is removing the single-use label from the on-the-go bottled beverage sector and advocates that their bottles be refilled. This is possible because PLA bottles don't contain the artificial chemicals that conventional PET bottles do.

Eco For Life is also the bottled water of choice for major UK festivals, where all bottles are collected after the event and are taken to a compost facility where they decompose into a rich soil supplement.

The founders are turning the tide on non-biodegradable plastic waste, but they are realistic. They know that it is a long road ahead, but this is the first step in the right direction.

65

PULP-TEC LIMITED, SCOTLAND

Wrapped Around Your Bottle

As a leading producer of molded pulp in Europe, Pulp-Tec offers a clever innovation with their flexi-wrap packaging sheets. Both elegant and practical by design, the flexi-wrap self-seals by inserting cubes from one part of the product to another, and wraps around fragile objects of any size or shape. This unique, strong design is useful and easy to assemble with interlocking cubes which absorb and cushion shocks in transit. It can fit a product of any size or shape, or can alternatively be used as a void fill. Edge protection can be fashioned to protect larger objects and furniture or small, fragile, or delicate items in transit.

You can test the strength of this product by standing on it – the Pulp-Tec team guarantees it won't crush!

Flexi-wrap is an excellent and ingenious alternative to polystyrene bubble-wrap, reducing the need for single-use plastics. All Pulp-Tec products offer a huge environmental benefit and are entirely eco-responsible. Waste paper and cardboard is converted to molded pulp using clean technology. The company follows circular design rules with a full lifecycle in mind – resulting in a totally endless lifespan! After use, the molded pulp products can be composted or returned to the paper recycling chain repeatedly, reducing waste and landfill pollution.

As a supplier of UN Approved Hazardous Chemical packaging for the safe transportation of glass bottles containing hazardous chemicals, the company guarantees that the packaging is resistant to transit vibration or shocks if dropped and has extraordinary mechanical crush resistance and stacking strength. This standard of quality offers unrivaled protection in transit packaging for spirit and wine packaging.

Gemma Acreman, Gary Shaw, Cameron Shaw, Pulp-Tec Limited, Scotland

LAMAZUNA, FRANCE

Avantgardist by Nature

Lamazuna was created by Laëtitia Van de Walle 10 years ago. At the time, she was becoming increasingly aware of the impact that our everyday waste was having on the environment. This gave her the idea of replacing her disposable cleansing wipes with an alternative that could be reused over 300 times, and ta-da! Lamazuna was born.

Over the years, the product range has grown and Lamazuna has become the leading brand for zero-waste accessories and vegan solid cosmetics made in France. Now, in addition to its reusable cleansing wipes, Lamazuna also offers solid shampoos, facial cleansers, menstrual cups, nail files, cocoa butter, solid deodorants, and its Oriculi ear cleaner – just about everything you could need for a zero-waste bathroom filled with natural products. They follow a 360° sustainable brand approach with initiatives going beyond the pure product focus. Manufacturing is mainly done locally and manually, and all products are 100 % vegan, plastic-free and cruelty-free.

Laëtitia Van de Walle, Bianca Lopes da Silva, Lamazuna France

67

NewPa – Immersions with Econscience

Creators Mónica, Bruno, and Rash believe that education is the basis of all change in our journey to a more sustainable world. Learn more about their initiative on page 146.

68

Helen Townsend,
New Zealand

HELEN TOWNSEND, NEW ZEALAND
The Rubbish Whisperer

In 2009, Helen Townsend was living and working in Nepal. She was appalled at the amount of unprocessed rubbish littering this beautiful country. On returning to New Zealand, she decided to reduce her own waste footprint and to create awareness around reusable and compostable products that can replace single-use plastics. Thus, the online platform 'The Rubbish Whisperer' was born.

The Rubbish Whisperer's reusable bags combine beauty with function and allow for a serious reduction in single-use plastics. The bags align with the four UN Sustainable Development Goals that Helen's initiative focuses on: Decent Work & Economic Growth, Sustainable Cities & Communities, Responsible Consumption & Production, Protect Life Below Water.

The bags have been designed to last for a long time. They don't have seams on the bottom, meaning they are less likely to break. The stretchy, lightweight fabric minimizes the number of bags required – one bag can hold a 3 kg pumpkin or a few cherry tomatoes. The fabric washes and dries easily and the light weave allows food to breathe, keeping it fresh for longer. Packaging is minimal and stylish, using recycled cards and a cleverly designed locking mechanism that eliminates the need for extra fixing materials. The bags are manufactured locally, employing a home-based workforce. Helen believes that by motivating people to take small steps, we can collectively make big changes that will help protect and preserve the delicate balance of our precious eco-systems.

*If we all take a small step,
we will all make a big change.*

Recycled Diaper Backpack

KIDDO is an innovative product inspired by Christina Nicholson from Cyprus. Their vision was to create a fully recycled, 2-in-1 diaper backpack for new-age, digital parents who want to carry their baby's belongings and their personal electronics. Nowadays, there is an abundance of diaper bags of all colors and sizes. None, however, appreciate that modern-day, eco-conscious parents want to be able to carry their baby's things and their digital gadgets together in a 'green' bag, comfortably. KIDDO does exactly that.

It is made of 100% recycled material and it is recyclable itself. KIDDO's material is recycled polyester made from 100% plastic bottles and produced using state-of-the-art, eco-friendly technology thus having the lowest possible environmental impact while still meeting demands for a durable, functional and stylish product.

Christina Nicholson,
Laidback Life, Cyprus

71

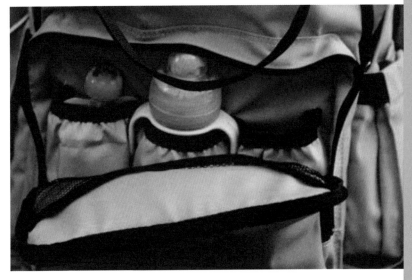

SAINBAGS, INDONESIA
I'm Not a Plastic Bag

SainBags is a growing, Indonesian-Oman-based company with its manufacturing and production facilities in Indonesia. It was founded in 2018 when the two entrepreneurs and environmentalists, Shradha Rungta and Husain Baomar, became tired of the waste created by plastic bags and decided there had to be a better way. Shortly after, they developed SainBags, an alternative to plastic bags made of natural cassava – a locally farmed, starchy yucca root.

SainBags are 100 % biodegradable and compostable, leaving no toxic residues. They cause no damage to the oceans or land and are harmless to animals and plants. The bags can safely return to nature in the form of water and carbon, and in turn feed the local agriculture, making it part of a truly sustainable lifecycle. SainBag's products do not contain a trace of plastic, therefore, do not contribute to the microplastics problem. The bags take around 90 days to compost in soil or a body of water, as opposed to hundreds of years for a regular Polyethylene bag. So far, one million single-use plastic bags have been replaced with this eco-responsible cassava alternative. Furthermore, the company is a responsible employer in their region and creates employee welfare and training for their workers.

Shradha Rungta,
Green bell Packaging UK,
Oman Oil GNC, Indonesia

TOBY ROBSON, UNITED KINGDOM

Drop

Drop is a solution created to reduce single-use plastic waste caused by milk portions found throughout restaurants, hotels, and other service industries around the world. It uses a food board container to hold portioned sizes of milk in packaging made from biodegradable seaweed, made by the sustainable packaging start-up Notpla. The packaging also meets high hygiene standards and prevents cross-contamination by releasing the portions one at a time.

Toby Robson,
University Project, United Kingdom

Peel Saver – Ecological Fries Packaging

A cool and eco-friendly street food packaging that replaces plasticized paper packaging. Learn more about this innovative material invented by Italian designers Pietro Gaeli, Simone Caronni, and Paolo Stefano Gentile on page 22.

CHARLIE CAVEDASCHI, UNITED KINGDOM

Shower Pods

Working part-time at a supermarket, Charlie Cavedaschi saw first-hand the amount of plastic-based packaging products used for food, cosmetics, toys, and toiletries. His research showed that bathroom waste from toiletry packaging accounts for 30 to 40% of total plastic waste, the most common being the ones for our shower and bathing routines. These frightening statistics, in addition to observing the amount of plastic bottled shampoo, conditioner, and shower gel in his own home, inspired him to explore a solution. Charlie knew he had to come up with a design that also solved the difficulty in controlling the right amount of liquid that's dispensed when squeezing the bottle, without adding further packaging to the product. After conducting further research, he found a material called MonoSol, a water-soluble film that produces zero waste.

The so-called 'Shower Pods' are solid, soluble toiletry balls of shampoo, conditioner, and shower gel, which are wrapped in a 3mm thick MonoSol film. Connected by perforations to a thicker structure for added support (which is also made of transparent film) these pods hang behind the showerhead giving an image of colored rainwater, whilst also keeping the shower area tidy. Wrapped in a deliberate teardrop shape, the Shower Pods can be easily torn off by the protruding tab with one hand, meaning there is no risk of the other pods dissolving. The thickness of the film has also been tested to withstand splashes of water and steam from the heat of the shower.

The pods take around five seconds to dissolve and leave zero waste. They are also a great replacement for travel toiletries. Being made from a solid material means there is no worry of the 100 ml liquid air travel restriction. Also, they free up space in your suitcase, as they're gone at the end of your trip leaving no bulky bottles behind.

Charlie Cavedaschi,
University Project, United Kingdom

Roads of Plastic

Let's build roads from old plastic bags! This is the motto of a research project conducted by the University of Wolverhampton. Plastic waste from old shopping carrier bags is processed as a binder for the production of low-cost paving block tiles. These tiles are suitable for hard-landscaping and pavement construction in light traffic roads.

This innovative process helps to reduce environmental pollution caused by plastic waste, in addition to the high-carbon footprint associated with the usage of conventional portland cement. The new polymer cementitious binder was systematically and scientifically obtained through a simple low-tech process that produces a strong adhesive and highly viscous liquid called 'molten polyethylene'. By using polymer modification methods, thermal blending, and casting processes, the molten polyethylene forms a quality polymer binder matrix for the aggregate filler. The resulting precast paving block samples were tested in a laboratory and displayed highly satisfactory engineering properties regarding strength and durability that supersede the standard requirements recommended by the British Standard Institute for Paving Block Tiles.

These innovative tiles represent a low-carbon, 'green', and sustainable alternative pavement construction material due to its zero cement content, zero water content, low production cost, repeated end-of-life recyclability, and re-usability. Researchers working on the project were pleased to find that this simple, low-tech solution can mitigate global environmental and economic issues, whilst remaining 'fit for purpose'.

Oriyomi Modupe Okeyinka, David A. Oloke,
United Kingdom

77

VESSEL, UNITED STATES
The Freeturnable Cup

Vessel helps communities and organizations to choose reusables! The start-up offers a circular economy solution for single-use plastic cups and takeaway boxes. The founders have created a cloud software-powered reusable cup and container service, which is redefining the status-quo of to-go, by inspiring people to ditch the throw-away culture with beautiful alternatives to single-use disposables. It is a holistic service system to help the public infrastructure to make reuse a reality for communities. Vessel's innovative, non-plastic, tech-enabled reusables system was launched in New York City in 2016. It has since expanded to Colorado and California, USA.

The Vessel cup elevates the user experience by making sustainability desirable with elegant, insulated stainless steel containers and 100% silicone lids. However, it is more than just a well-designed cup. It is an Internet-Of-Things reusables service that effectively addresses the problem of disposables. The service delivers transparency through automatic impact feedback to users, giving them an update on the significant impacts of their everyday consumption choices to enable a rapid transition to a sustainable lifestyle. Vessel is the trojan horse that gets people to ditch the disposable mindset!

Dagny Tucker, Founder
Quin Raderstorf, Bay Area Logistics and Outreach Manager
Trinity Wells, CFO,
United States

3DTOMORROW, UNITED KINGDOM
Ecological 3D Printing

The 3D printing industry is growing rapidly, particularly in the hobbyist sector. The majority of this user base operates a type of 3D printer which uses spools of raw filament to fabricate products. 3D Printing is what's known as additive manufacturing. It starts with nothing and adds layers of material to build up the product. This process is inherently very efficient since it results in much less wastage than traditional subtractive manufacturing like CNC machining, where you grind away particles from a solid metal block. If the supplies of 3D printing filament are responsibly sourced, then this method could represent one of the best manufacturing technologies from an environmental standpoint. Unfortunately, most filaments supplied today are not manufactured in line with high sustainability standards. Firstly, a lot of filament is manufactured overseas, creating a high carbon footprint due to the long transportation. Secondly, the filament is supplied on black plastic spools, which are not able to be recycled by local sorting facilities, meaning around 20% of the supplied product is destined for landfill.

The British start-up 3DTomorrow offers an alternative. Their flagship filament material Eco PLA contains up to 70% recycled material, is supplied on a 100% recyclable cardboard spool and contains the bare minimum in packaging. The founders at 3DTomorrow also encourage their customers to reuse the cardboard spool. PLA (Polylactic acid) is a fantastic alternative to petroleum-based plastics because it is a renewable material made from corn starch. The recycled content used in Eco PLA further improves the carbon footprint. The material is matte and produced in a range of soft colors, meaning it is destined to create beautiful and long-lasting objects.

Callum Coles,
3DTomorrow, United Kingdom

MOST BEAUTIFUL SOLUTIONS

In this category, we present solutions for a world with less plastic which are aesthetic, appealing, lovely, eye-catching, elegant, exquisite, artistic, marvelous, musing, ravishing, exquisite, pretty, divine, desirable, enticing, fascinating, well-formed, picturesque, striking, colorful and breathtaking.

82

113

Shell Homage – Bio Material Out of Egg & Nut Shells

Shell Homage is a biodegradable composite material made from egg and nut shells. It contains no toxic chemicals, is completely biodegradable, and is 100% compostable when no longer used. It can be applied in several industries such as product design, interior design, 3D filament consumable goods, and jewelry design. It's the ultimate solution for getting rid of things instead of storing them for years and getting rid of oil-based plastics, which never decay.

Shell Homage was founded by the integrated designer Rania Elkalla and was initiated during her master's research project. Rania can control the material properties according to the application – from stiff, hard, transparent, translucent, or opaque surfaces to elastic and malleable sheets. The surfaces look like marble or natural stone, but the substance is much lighter. The created composite material can be pressed, extruded, 3D printed, or formed by injection molding. Each surface is handcrafted into a unique combination of colors and patterns.

GOLD AWARD WINNER
Rania Elkalla, Shell Homage, Germany

Coffee Talk with Rania

Please tell us about yourself, Rania! I am the founder of Shell Homage. As an integrated designer with a product and graphic design background, I am also experienced in material science and production techniques. Initially, I studied product design and industrial design and learned about the idea of integrated design when studying at KISD, the Köln International School of Design. Then I went on to do my master's at the Polymer Science Institute, TU Berlin. My work can be described as eclectic. I love traveling and getting exposed to different cultures and styles and merging between different disciplines. Also, I like to design things with humor and interaction with users. I had a passion for material from a very young age – being a person who loves to touch things, explore the surfaces of things – and always likes to explore the things around me.

How did you come up with the idea for your Shell Homage project? It actually came by coincidence. I was inspired by my father who always likes to buy fresh nuts from the local market and crack them open at home. Being astounded by how strong the shells were I started analyzing the material to use in design. Then the same thing happened with eggs. We liked to have a family breakfast together, where we often ate eggs and I became fascinated with the shells. I started collecting egg shells from friends, from local bakeries, and then went on to get them from restaurants. I wanted to change the perception of food waste so that the user doesn't really know what the material's origin is – was it nut or egg shells? And then when you know you have this 'Aha!' moment. I like playing with a material and to change the perception of it.

Where do you see the future for Shell Homage? I'm currently producing materials and also creating examples out of this material for my other products. Also, I would love to collaborate with different designers, whether in the interior design industry or even fashion or jewelry to scale up the material so that it can be more accessible to different people in different countries. I've also started to use the material as a 3D printing filament, but not yet on a commercial basis. My goal is to make it accessible because it's a very interesting material when you 3D print it.

How did you achieve the remarkable media coverage? Any tips for us? I've been really lucky in terms of marketing. I entered competitions and after winning received a lot of publicity. There was even a German TV documentary produced! We did street interviews and asked people "What do you think of this material?" and no one really knew it was egg or nut shells. My tip would be to keep applying for international competitions. Even if you don't win, you will usually get feedback. It's good to expose your idea to see how it works compared to others and see what people think of it. Furthermore, Shell Homage had the chance to participate in several fairs where people can experience the material and give feedback and this really helps a lot.

PAULA NERLICH, GERMANY

Aqua Faba Foam

Material Designer Paula Nerlich is developing a bioplastic based on aquafaba from chickpeas as part of her research into circular, compostable biomaterials.

The material, which is currently under development, shows great potential for mechanical manufacturing and thus for industrial production. The biomaterial varies in color from cream white to pink and changes its color over time. However, it can be dyed with natural or food colors. The structure can be flexible or hard, the recipe is adaptable. The biomaterial is completely vegan and biodegradable. Compostability is currently being tested.

The temporary nature of biodegradable biomaterials reminds us of the flow of nature and makes us appreciate the quality of impermanence. The transience of the materials has the potential to create a higher value in the end product, while also emphasizing the circular nature of the material.

SILVER AWARD WINNER
Paula Nerlich, Designer & Co-Founder Circular Home Lab, Germany

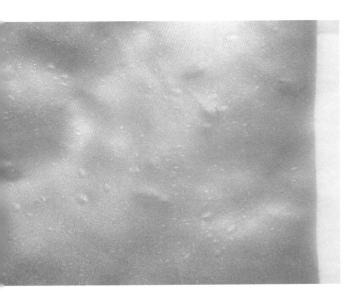

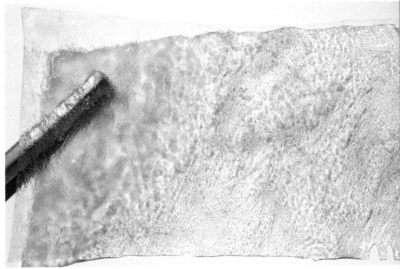

Coffee Talk with Paula 🎧 ·I|I·I||I·I||I·I||I·I|·

Please tell us about yourself and your sustainability journey.
I'm a Material Designer living in Berlin currently. I have a background in Textile Design and moved towards sustainable materials design exploring and creating new biomaterials from food waste. Apart from doing that, I'm starting my PhD at the moment, researching how to create structures with living materials. When I was a child, I decided to become a vegetarian and I think that was when I became more aware of everything being connected in the living world and sustainability being a crucial part of that. I took a few turns. I started with fashion and discovered that it's so unsustainable. Then I continued to study textiles, finding new ways of creating materials with raw sustainable ingredients.

Can you tell us how you created the Aqua Faba Foam?
The aim was to incorporate a by-product from food production and I chose aquafaba, the starchy liquid that you get as a byproduct from cooking chickpeas. I did two things – I wanted to create something beautiful and I wanted to create my own recipe. I experimented a lot and one day I had a bioplastic-like material. I started creating prototypes with clients and I'm continuously trying to find a way to get this material refined and manufactured. That is the ultimate goal of any material designer within the Biodesign community. Many of us create our materials and might not manage to bring them to the market, or we decide to use the material to create statement pieces and use it for communication, design, and art. Ultimately, I would like to get it manufactured on a slightly larger scale, not too large because when you work with food production byproducts, you need to be aware of the limited resource.

What do you see as the biggest obstacles going into production? To go into production, you need a really large budget and part of that budget would be needed to get certificates. If we're looking at packaging, we might need a food safety certificate. We will need a lab testing of all the properties, so I guess the main challenges are funding and production partners that are open to explore new materials. And if you produce packaging, it needs to be part of some sort of recycling stream. The local waste management systems do not necessarily yet embrace those new materials depending on where you are. One has to ask: Can the biomaterial be composted? Is that household compost or is it industrial composting? Will it get recycled or reused?

What do you think we can do to solve the plastic pollution problem on a large scale? I think I would go back to the communication issue. There have been a lot of amazing campaigns that have changed so much. The plastic pollution problem has gained a lot of awareness from people, but it's not yet enough. I think what BEYONDPLASTIC is doing, for example, is really relevant, because we need to continue to talk to all the different participants, not only the end-users but also manufacturers, big corporations, and so on. It's still a long journey, but I think talking about it and showing potential alternatives will really change the way we do things and help in the long run, although we're running out of time so we need to do it rather quickly. It's about changing our patterns and gaining and exchanging knowledge to sustainably create change.

MARGARITA TALEP, CHILE

Desintegra.me

This biomaterials project intends to replace single-use plastics with a new substance extracted from algae. The Spanish term "Desintegra me" implies that it will 'disappear' after use. Pigments are extracted from the skin of discarded fruit and vegetables.

The material can have different degrees of flexibility – it can be rigid and brittle to flexible and elastic. It degrades naturally over a period of two to four months depending on the atmospheric conditions.

BRONZE AWARD WINNER
Margarita Talep,
Industrial Designer, Chile

Coffee Talk with Margarita

Tell us in a few words: Who are you? What do you do?
I'm Margarita Talep, a designer based in Santiago, Chile. I develop projects related to sustainability, nature, and new materials.

What motivated you to get into sustainability? Was it a particular moment or a gradual process? It was a gradual process. Before studying design there were topics that were discussed in my social life or family circle. They are subjects that I'm passionate about and that interest me enormously. During my studies, the design academy gave me the tools to work around my interests in an innovative, creative way and with great freedom. Since I can see the world from the designer's point of view, social, political, cultural, and environmental issues take on greater importance in the way we develop projects - of whatever type - and I think that's what sustainability is all about.

How did you come up with your idea? Everything started with milk. In a workshop at university, the topic of the semester was "biopolymers". We were required to work in pairs, so my colleague and I arrived at our first class with several polymer test tubes of things that had interested us. Inside them was casein, the protein in milk. We ended up developing a milk-based bioplastic that had incredible results. This project was the starting point that motivated me to continue developing a series of experiments with natural polymers over time. When it was time to start the annual project, I questioned whether using milk was a viable way to develop what I had in mind, so I looked for polymer alternatives that were not of animal origin. I wanted a raw material that was found locally in abundance and one where the extraction was not harmful to ecosystems. So that summer I started an experiment with algae. I already knew a lot about it in theory, so I was able to quickly create an interesting test tube with potential for further development.

What are your future plans for your project? The project was in the stage of productive viability and the long and extensive research that this entails. Due to COVID-19, this has been paused. I hope the future of this project will show that this material can be produced and be used on smaller scales whilst taking care of the extraction of the raw material and the method in which this is done. For example, in Chile, it is expected that seaweed cultivation in sandbanks will increase in the coming years. This would allow the natural ocean grasslands to be regenerated and not cause damage to the ecosystem. We must be careful with all the variables. The most important thing is that the material can coexist in harmony with its ecosystem.

What are the biggest obstacles you face?
There are a few obstacles. For example, in Chile, it is difficult to obtain the finances to continue developing these materials. So overall it is a difficult path and a lot of effort but I believe eventually it can have great results.

What do you think we can do to solve the plastic pollution problem? I believe that we can stop the plastic pollution problem with a universe of diverse solutions and initiatives, be they social, cultural, economic, innovative, educational. No matter how small our changes in habits or customs, all together they will help to solve plastic pollution.

87

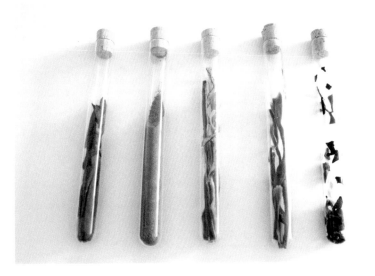

88

Starch and Fibres – Material Studies

This compound material is water-soluble and has been
sealed with a layer of natural resin. Before sealing, the material
can be sanded and polished to a high gloss. Learn more about
Johannes Bauer's innovative studies on page 32.

KSONI, UNITED KINGDOM

Shampoo in a Can

When Joti Sohi and Banasa Williams first met in 2018, they decided to launch a natural beauty brand. They were setting themselves a huge challenge to launch a 100 % plastic-free product, which is no easy feat in the bathroom. From there KSONI was born.

KSONI is a sustainable body care brand designed to extend the eco-mindset from the kitchen to the bathroom via unique, plastic-free packaging. The aim is to offer consumers the opportunity to access premium and natural bathroom products whilst simultaneously reducing their use of single-use plastics. Ultimately, the creators of KSONI want to make a positive impact on the fight against plastic waste and embrace the circular economy. After months of testing and prototyping, Joti and Banasa are proud to have launched their shampoos and body washes in the humble aluminum can.

Key Features:
- 100 % plastic-free packaging
- 100 % natural ingredients, that actually work
- Products are infused with essential oils chosen for their specific hair, skin, and mood benefits
- Suitable for a wide range of hair and skin types
- Proprietary/bespoke cap which allows the can to be closed and sealed after taking a shower

Joti Sohi, Banasa Williams,
KSONI, United Kingdom

UNIVERSITY PROJECT, GERMANY

Alinde – Water Carafe

Barbara Fischer and Luise Münzner studied Product Design at the Bauhaus University in Weimar where they conducted a critical examination of our product culture. They investigated responsible design with regards to social and sustainable added value in contemporary design.

With the glass carafe 'Alinde' they reinterpret traditional craftsmanship. The language of form shows a synthesis of contemporary design and prototyping tools with centuries old knowledge. A permanent exchange and a close cooperation with the glass blowers led to added value on different levels.

The carafe allows the water to be filtrated and this functionality is implemented into its flowing design. The highly concave spout provides a secure yet loose hold for the floating carbon filter. Thanks to the activated carbon stick inside the carafe, harmful substances are absorbed from the water and an unadulterated, soft taste is created.

The function reflects the natural composition of the glass, which is processed using 100 % natural raw materials. After extensive research and careful examination of glass as a material, the focus was on health and well-being. Initially, digital tools were used to create forms and models on screen, which were then printed in 3D. This made it possible to test prototypes quickly, which, thanks to further trials and constant consultation with the glassmakers, led to an ever greater degree of maturity and eventually a beautiful final product.

91

Barbara Fischer, Luise Münzner,
Product Designer, Germany

Rahel Mor,
Industrial Design Student, Switzerland

92

RAHEL MOR, SWITZERLAND
From Coffee for Coffee

During a stay in Kenya, Rahel Mor visited the Chania Coffee Estate in Thika. This is one of the oldest estates in the country, where some of the coffee bushes are believed to be 100 years old. Similar to grapevine, coffee bushes require regular pruning. The discarded branches are put aside as firewood. Rahel wanted to bring some coffee back as a gift for friends but needed a unique packaging. She was inspired by the wood of the coffee bushes – it was exquisite – hard, of dark honey color and often had a beautiful texture.

Rachel created glass jars by cutting off the tops of wine bottles, which are readily available, as glass bottles are not recycled in Kenya. The wooden lids for the cut bottles, now jars, are turned on a lathe from the coffee wood. The lid serves a dual purpose, as a lid to the jar and as a coffee tamper for the espresso machine. For an authentic African-designed lid, Rahel took inspiration from the Mokorotlo, the traditional woven hats of the Lesotho people. She then went on to create a wide array of shapes.

This whole process can be carried out locally in Kenya which offers many benefits. Firstly, the coffee jars are not just 'nice to haves' but they can create meaningful employment for the community. In addition, loose coffee can be found in not just specialty shops but supermarkets too, with the majority available in disposable plastic packaging. With Rachel's coffee jars, people can bring their own containers to refill in-store and avoid unnecessary packaging and plastic waste. Then at home, they have a beautiful piece of art in their kitchen!

Wild Plastic

As a South Florida resident, Phil Scarlata is constantly at the beach, so ocean plastic pollution is close to home. Swimming and diving in plastic debris fueled his drive to create a plastic pollution prevention company, and so Wild Plastic was born.

The essence of Wild Plastic is to create a purpose for end-of-life plastic pollution found in the environment, as opposed to selling it back to plastic manufacturers that create more single-use plastic. With the plastic Phil recovers, he creates unique and valuable household products that can be used infinitely to ensure zero plastic waste. His motto is: "The less plastic in the wild or at landfills the better".

The team at Wild Plastic has built their own machines to create value from the plastic waste they collect. The process begins with cleaning, sorting, and then shredding the recovered plastic to create flakes. The next step is to either extrude the flakes around a custom mold to create Upcycled Bowls and Baskets, or to inject the flakes into a mold to create their so-called Awareness Coasters. The plastic used has no added dyes or materials and the colors used are the original colors of the plastic they recover.

Through awareness, clean-ups, upcycling, supplying alternatives, and donating to like-minded organizations, Phil believes we all can make a difference to our oceans and he hopes to see the benefits in years to come.

Phil Scarlata,
Wild Plastic, United States

AWARENESS
COASTERS
UPCYCLED FROM 100% LOCALLY RECOVERED
RECYCLED PLASTIC
TYPE: HDPE
$15

93

WILD PLASTIC

Coolpaste

Coolpaste is a sustainable packaging
design that literally thinks outside the box.
Designer Allan Gomes has conceived an
eco-friendly alternative to the humble
toothpaste tube. Learn more on page 50.

Jennifer Chu,
Designer, United Kingdom

JENNIFER CHU, UNITED KINGDOM

Be a Pastaholic, Not a Plastoholic!

Porzioni Di Pasta, meaning 'Portions of Pasta' in Italian, is a carton-board packaging solution for dried pasta that today is often packaged in non-recyclable, single-use plastic.

The idea not only focuses on sustainability, but also on portion control. Using a tear-away strip, pasta lovers can pour the pasta into the lid, which acts as a measuring cup for one suggested serving of approximately 75 g. This is for one serving, but it can be used to measure for groups of people, too. Additionally, the measuring lid is suitable for various pasta shapes and sizes.

The packaging design features each unique pasta shape and takes inspiration from the Memphis art movement whilst using futuristic color palettes. Every pack is bold and colorful, making it stand out from usual pasta packaging. The hexagonal prism shape allows for easy stacking during transportation, but also on supermarket shelves, whether it is vertical or horizontal.

WILD, SCOTLAND

Go Green, Go Wild!

Wild is a natural deodorant company that focuses on performance, sustainability, and style. They utilize the powers of the natural world to create an effective, long-lasting deodorant that is free of aluminum and parabens whilst also being cruelty-free and vegan. The stylish and reusable Wild applicator is made from durable aluminum and recycled plastic, to ensure it stands the test of time. Meanwhile, their natural deodorant is 100 % biodegradable, making it a zero-plastic deodorant refill.

Wild offers five fresh scents to fit every mood; Coconut Dreams, Mint Fresh, Rose Blush, Bergamot Rituals, and Orange Zest.

TOP 20

Harry Symes-Thompson,
Childhood friends, Freddy & Charlie,
Wild, Scotland

OZEANO VISION, AUSTRALIA
Eco-Friendly Sunglasses

Mark Cason,
Ozeano Vision, Australia

Australian company Ozeano Vision provides sunglasses with frames made from a 100% biodegradable, plant-based bio-acetate, along with 100% GOTS-certified organic cotton pouches and FSC-certified cork cases. Their products are handmade locally in New South Wales, Australia, and all their packaging is 100% biodegradable and compostable. They use carbon-neutral shipping to deliver every product that's sold.

Ozeano Vision has partnered with the Australian Seabin Project, a revolutionary ocean cleaning technology that aims to create cleaner oceans and healthier marine life.

Finally, they donate a proportion of their sales to Sight For All; a charity project which offers eye health services in local communities that previously didn't have access to these medical treatments.

FONDIUM GROUP GMBH, GERMANY

Sustainable BBQ With Style

FONDIUM is an iron casting foundry that has embedded sustainability into their manufacturing process. They use sand molds and sand cores made of recycled, raw, and reusable materials for their cast components. The casted safety parts are also made of recycled materials and are 100 % recyclable after use. These practices certify FONDIUM as a green foundry.

Initially, FONDIUM predominantly made cast iron parts for the automobile industry. They have recently started to develop a new market segment for consumer goods under the brand name IGNIUM. One of the first products to be launched will be an eco-friendly barbecue set.

The IGNIUM barbecue set will be made solely from recyclable material, like cast iron, in combination with sustainably grown wood. It will also be made locally in Germany to reduce the carbon footprint.

The BBQ comes in plastic-free packaging made of cardboard and is designed in such a way that the customer will find each product part in the correct order of assembly. The innovative packaging can also be reused to store the barbecue during winter, or it can be recycled at home. The very simple but clever packaging system does not require any plastic material to keep the parts in position.

Fabian Maier,
FONDIUM Group GmbH, Germany

99

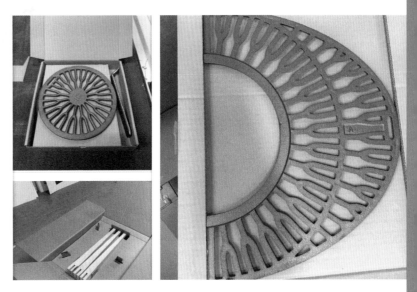

MELINA KRAUSS, GERMANY

teasy – Tea Very Easy

Melina Krauß is a German product designer with a passion for developing solutions for everyday life. She comes from East Frisia on the northern coast of Germany. It's said to be the capital of German tea culture, where locals say "First, let's have a cup of tea and then let's see". No wonder, that Melina is a tea lover! Inspired by her passion for tea, she created teasy, her answer to the plastic tea bag problem.

The teasy tea strainer isn't just timeless, because of its minimal design, but also because of its use of food-safe stainless steel. In addition, teasy has a long lifespan and can be used over and over again, making it very durable and sustainable.

Melina Krauß,
Product Designer, Germany

With teasy, freshly brewed tea is quite easy in the blink of an eye. The strainer opens by rotation and can be filled according to demand, whether it be a pot or a cup. Close teasy again and give the leaves space to infuse the water with their full flavor. After the steeping time, teasy can be taken out. By rotating the lid 180°, the tea leaves are pushed from the hemisphere leaving little mess. This clever product reduces the need for disposable plastic and represents an ecological solution for everyday life.

LITTLE PINK MAKER, DENMARK

MaterialeX

Chan'nel Vestergaard is a British expat living in Copenhagen who is 100% passionate about crafting, science and sustainability. She's been crafting since the age of six, and studied textiles and design, before moving into science and technology at MIT, Boston. Cha'nel founded Little Pink Maker in 2017, which holds creative workshops in mixing craft with science, sustainability, and fun. The creative team at Little Pink Maker consists of self-taught scientists and their motto is "Science is there for all".

Chan'nel created MaterialeX; a beautiful biomaterials kit that contains ten recipes. The kit teaches basic chemistry, Do-It-Yourself Biomaterial Design, and encourages discussions about eco-innovation whilst being playful and hands-on.

The kit is handmade locally in Copenhagen in a co-creative maker space as a source of inspiration. Everything about MaterialeX is either biodegradable or biocompostable. It gives users a new perspective on waste, by making materials from it, and helps them to and understand material streams and circular processes.

Chan'nel Vestergaard,
Little Pink Maker, Denmark

*Innovation happens
when we think outside the box.*

Cladophora – A Water Saving Resource

Can the increasing growth of algae be used for material development? Yes! Learn more about Malu Lücking's innovative textile material on page 24.

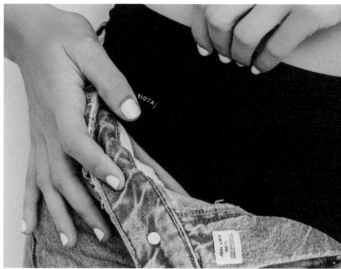

BIOTA, COLOMBIA
Biota Eco Wear

Laura Villanueva,
Biota, Colombia

Laura Villanueva from Colombia is an entrepreneur with a passion for sustainability and refuses to conform to the breach of inequality. She founded Biota Eco Wear, a company that designs and manufactures women's underwear.

Biota garments are composed of 45% rPET bottles and 50% recovered cotton. When you wear Biota, you're feeling soft and comfortable underwear made from recycled materials that are good for your body and the environment. The subtle use of elastic threading creates comfortable garments that can be worn for leisure, working out, or going out. By using recycled polyester Biota gives a second life to a material that's not biodegradable and would otherwise end up in landfills or the ocean.

Every design features unique, detailed patterns and is carefully cut into perfectly fitting pieces to accommodate all sizes. The pieces are handmade by eight women in a boutique workshop in Medellin, Colombia. Laura's dream is to grow her start-up with women from Tasajera, an abandoned but beautiful town.

ITAC, MEXICO
Give and Take

The name ITAC comes from the Aztecan language Nahuatl 'itacatl' which refers to the action of giving or getting a portion of food to be eaten at a later time. ITAC is a reusable container designed to hold food such as seeds, chili peppers, cereals, or spices in bulk. It is designed to help people contribute to the process of Use, Reuse, and Recycle.

ITAC is made of 70% multi-layer cardboard that comes from renewable wood in combination with residual materials from different industries, giving stability, strength, and flexibility to the container. Foil paper protects the food from oxygen and light and polyethylene protects it from exterior and interior humidity which improves resistance and allows for multi-use.

ITAC differs itself from other containers because the packaging allows room for local food producers to advertise. This clever packaging box contributes towards reducing plastic bag production, use, and waste. It's recommended for six months of use or 50 refills.

Nidia García Arévalo,
ITAC, Mexico

105

Tanya Vulfson,
Graphic Designer, United States

TANYA VULFSON, UNITED STATES

Let's Spoon

Spudlery is spud cutlery. These single-use utensils are made from potato starch and soy oil. These days, plastic alternatives are a future-forward solution to our pollution problem. In fact, it is hard to imagine there was ever a time before plastic. That's why Tanya Vulfson designed a line of potato-based utensils inspired by the pre-plastic era, including rubber hose cartoons, 1920s boxing posters, and the retro aesthetic of low-cost printing methods.

The young designer's project directly addresses the marketability of plastic alternatives by creating a visual identity with a fun, appealing twist.

WILDPLASTIC, GERMANY
Recovered From Nature

WILDPLASTIC was started by a team of activists who saw the damage that plastic does to our environment. They wondered why, if there are so many materials out there, we are still producing virgin plastic instead of recycling and reusing the resource we have dumped in nature? WILDPLASTIC worked out a solution. They source plastic from beaches, landfills, and illegal dumpsites and work with communities of collectors around the world to bring these materials back into the production cycle, preventing them from ending up in the environment.

WILDPLASTIC collects plastic in countries where waste management and recycling is problematic or non-existing. They initiate, build and co-operate with Non-Government Organizations and collectives to clean the environment and create innovative products where plastic meets its recyclable future, piece by piece. WILDPLASTIC's first product is a trash bag, called WILDBAG. Every bag is made from 100% collected plastic from the environment and is designed to raise awareness.

Nadia Boegli, Christian Sigmund, Holger Ernst, Fridtjof Detzner, Dieter Gottschalk, Jascha Mähler, Katrin Oeding, Wildplastic, Germany

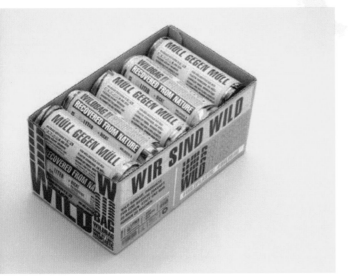

The Everyday Plastic Survey

The Everyday Plastic Survey was founded by Daniel Webb, who collected every piece of plastic waste he generated for a whole year. Read more about his personal journey that became a fun and interactive initiative for everyone on page 141.

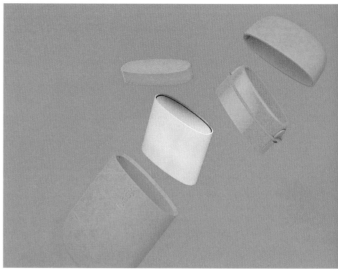

FUSSY, UNITED KINGDOM
Feeling Fussy?

Fussy is a refillable natural deodorant in a beautiful container. It's made entirely from recycled plastic bottles and includes plastic-free refills made from waste bamboo that you can compost at home. Throughout its lifetime, each product will prevent the equivalent of more than 2 kg of single-use plastic. The team at the young start-up worked hard to make sure Fussy had the lowest possible impact on the planet.

The deodorant container has a beautiful organic shape — the designers took inspiration from a pebble on the beach. It also comes in a range of bright, modern colors.

Fussy uses a letterbox format to ensure that it can be used by existing postal delivery routes, minimizing our environmental impact further.

Matt Kennedy, Eddie Fisher,
Fussy, United Kingdom

A Toothbrush That Cares About You and the Planet

EcoTooth is dedicated to designing and manufacturing quality, eco-friendly, sustainable lifestyle products at affordable prices. They give people the power to help change the world each time they brush their teeth and to positively impact the environment as well as their lifestyle.

The design team created Tooth as a super sleek and modern take on the manual brush. The Tooth's handle is made from recycled aluminum and the head is detachable and biodegradable. The body of the head is made from Floreon, a bioplastic made from locally sourced sugar beets, and the bristles are Nylon 4, a biodegradable compound of Nylon. Tooth comes with various accessories including a travel case made from BPA-free recycled plastic, a storage case, and three additional biodegradable heads. Built inside the case is a recycled magnet, allowing you to attach the brush to the stainless steel toothbrush stand.

Kiana Guyon, Co-Founder & CCO
Joshua Oates, Co-Founder & CEO,
Eco Tooth, United Kingdom

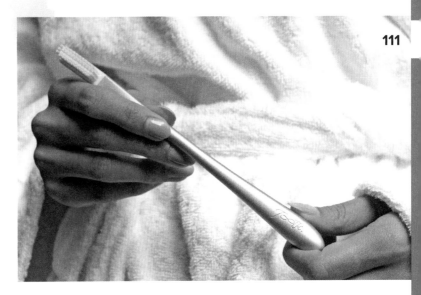

111

Biopod
DownWool
Nature

aus 100% Natur

GRÜEZI BAG, GERMANY

Say Grüezi to a Woolen Sleeping Bag

Grüezi bag is a young company located close to the Bavarian Alps. The founders believe in the importance of sleeping well while traveling, so they designed sleeping bags with maximum comfort. Additionally, they wanted to create a sleeping bag made from 100 % natural materials – from the packaging down to the very last button and they succeeded! Their Biopod DownWool Nature sleeping bag is made without any plastic or metal. There is no need for a zipper because wooden buttons are used and the packaging is made from cardboard.

After spending a night in a Grüezi bag, campers have been impressed by the quality sleeping conditions and the sense of well-being. For extra comfort, you can adjust the bag's width, and it also comes with a convenient pillow pocket.

Grüezi bag uses its own proven DownWool filling for insulation; it is a combination of down and wool to make an innovative new material. An intensive development phase was needed to combine the materials naturally. It harnesses the benefits of both materials in one innovative product: wool, which works like natural air conditioning and is damp resistant, and down, which offers high insulation and is very light-weight. This is glamping (glamorous camping) at its unadulterated best. Grüezi bag brings your bed at home to the campground.

Markus Wiesböck,
Grüezi bag, Germany

ALEXANDRA WARTHA, AUSTRIA

Don't Waste Your Life

Alexandra Wartha is a passionate designer from Austria with a socio-ecological mindset.

Her project "Don't waste your life" is a five-part poster series on the topic "Weapons of the Design Revolution". What's left when we leave? No, it's not beautiful sandy beaches, deep green forests, and cute little puppies. It's plastic. What can we do about it? What do we do about the waste?

The poster series is an artistic expression that brings abstract plastic waste mountains into concrete form. It conveys that plastic is like a weapon that we point at ourselves. The artwork was created during a workshop in Berlin using plastic trash and black acrylic paint to make collages. The slogan "Don't waste your life" expresses, that each individual can make a contribution to the protection of our environment. Sustainability begins in our minds. Every small change can make a big difference. Let's get started!

Alexandra Wartha, Communication Designer Concept & Design,
Johannes Ebner, Description,
Austria

BEST INITIATIVES

In this category, we present solutions for a world with less plastic that are inspiring, educational, informative, ambitious, energetic, adventurous, enthusiastic, fresh, venturesome, quick-witted, memorable, thrilling, excellent, insightful, wise, wild, provocative, and uncomfortable truthful.

INDIVIDUAL INITIATIVE, BULGARIA

Choose the Reusable Cup

In Bulgarian public kindergartens, children between 3–7 years of age drink water almost exclusively from disposable plastic cups. As a result, the annual plastic waste equals 250 million cups, weighs 550 tons, and would cover half of the Earth's Equator, if wasted cups were arranged in a line. This is an extreme case of throw-away culture that is being imprinted into children's perceptions as a norm. From an economic standpoint, the produced waste costs Bulgarian citizens between 3 – 3.5 million Euros per year.

The "Choose the Reusable Cup" project started as a local community initiative in a state kindergarten in the town of Varna, Bulgaria. Sabina Maksimova, a mother of two, proposed a solution: A reusable metal cup engraved with a unique symbol for each child. Later, this community initiative received the support of a local ecology organization – The Public Environmental Center for Sustainable Development. Currently, the project has the ambitious task to reach parent communities across the whole country.

The mission of the "Choose the Reusable Cup" project is to change perceptions and consumption norms so that caring about the environment and healthy living will be more valued than the few-seconds-convenience of the disposable container.

GOLD AWARD WINNER
Sabina Maksimova, Ilian Iliev, Evgenia Tasheva

Coffee Talk with Sabina

Please could you tell us about yourself, Sabina! I'm a 39-year-old mother of two young daughters. Professionally, I'm a marketing manager. In terms of my personal convictions, I am a confessed ecology fan. I am very much concerned about the future of the planet. In Bulgaria there is a saying when something bad happens, "Don't worry, it's not the end of the world!". Now being a grown-up, I see that there are things that are changing our world forever and I really want to turn the tide on all these negative changes and do something good about the environment, for my children and everybody else ... and for future generations.

How did you get into eco-responsible activities? I have always been interested in this. When I was a child, I used to clean up the local gardens, when I saw garbage on the ground. But motherhood was the turning point for me when I decided to do something very special about my green life and the environment. When I became a mom I was surprised to see that my child suffered from allergies. So I started researching about the causes of allergies and I found out that the cause lies to a great extent in the polluted environment. I learned that in the human body, including in breast milk, there are many artificial substances coming from artificial compounds used in plastic. That was a turning point in my decision to engage in a long-lasting project about plastic prevention. When my first child got into kindergarten we were asked to bring a huge amount of single-use plastic cups. I asked why, and they said, there are very strict hygiene requirements and this is why we need single-use plastic cups. I think the view that throwaway plastic is highly hygienic is a misconception. It's actually bad propaganda among the population fueled by the industry. There is a huge financial interest in convincing people to buy new single-use things, throw them away and buy new ones. This is a nightmare. I believe in three components of hygiene and keeping things clean: soap, water, and heat. Besides the plastic pollution problem, I think plastic is unhealthy because of the many artificial substances included which can cause allergies and other health issues.

Was it hard to convince the other parents in the kindergarten? When this project started, I managed to convince the parents in my Kindergarten group. But it took time and hot debate because we had to change 'the norm': in Bulgaria, almost all kindergartens use these single-use plastic cups, which amount to 250 million cups per year. After the successful implementation of reusable cups in our group I said, okay, more and more parents should know that there is a viable alternative to the single-use plastic cups. We managed to convince over 4,500 children from 20 different towns in Bulgaria to join the program. And, we have done this alone with no financial support from anywhere. The fuel of this project is this incentive, this motivation, this love for children, the love for nature, and that there is such an easy solution to problems like plastic pollution.

And what's been the children's response to using the cups? We involve three-year-old children who are switching from a bottle to a cup for the first time. We really want their first switch to be to a reusable cup and not to a single-use plastic one so they do learn to reuse the things around them. These are the basic years when people learn their habits and form their views. They're very sweet and cute in their reaction. They love their cups. They surprise their teachers because they get used to their own cups with their unique pictures from the very start.

INDIVIDUAL INITIATIVE, ZAMBIA
U-RETAIN

Plastic waste remains one of the mainland pollutants in Lusaka, and Zambia as a whole. The use and dumping of plastic materials in the streets of most communities is extreme. However, in a society full of plastic waste materials and developing recycling companies, it's paramount to find a means of linking the less privileged and recycling companies. The You Retain, spelled as U-Retain is an environmental initiative that seeks to use plastics as purchasing power for educational basics such as books, pencils, pens, school uniforms, school bags, school shoes and help adolescents in examinations classes pay their examination fee. Furthermore, the initiative also allows children living on the streets and the less privileged to buy light foodstuffs and sanitary pads using plastics.

The aim of the initiative is to add more value to plastic waste materials so that people can exchange them for basic needs. The collected plastics are sold to recycling companies at a reasonable monetary amount. The initiative will engage more with community schools and government schools and will put up U-Retain Booths in places that have

a lot of plastic waste materials. At its early stage and later stage, the initiative should be able to make money vis-a-vis the sale of collected plastic waste materials and be able to benefit the engaged audience through providing educational and school materials. Besides that, it will also be able to help a good number of homeless children access sanitary pads and light meals.

GOLD AWARD WINNER
John Emmanuel Kachakwale, Beatrice Phiri,
Photograph: Fredrick Chilongo and DMS production,
Individual Initiative, Zambia

118

Coffee Talk with John Emmanuel

Please tell us a little about yourself, John! My name is John Emmanuel Kachakwale. I am 23 years old and pursuing my bachelor's degree in Arts of Mass Communication and Public Relations at Cavendish University in Zambia. Besides that, I am an activist and advocate for the environment related to social health and youth advocacy.

How did your journey as an environmentalist start? I never saw myself getting involved with activism and advocacy when I was younger. It all started in 2013 when my high-school Geography teacher selected me to be trained to be a Child Climate Ambassador at the Zambia Children Climate Conference. The training included various environmental and climate change sessions and for me, it was socially interesting because we were a group of 75 children from different parts of Lusaka. Weirdly, the training itself did not ignite a spark to start something but after the training, I had memories of my time back in Kabwe, one of the most polluted cities because it's based around the mining industry. The water and land are contaminated with toxic lead. I currently live in Lusaka where many people don't have clean water and travel long distances to get water. Sometimes we would wake up around 4 o'clock in the morning to go and queue for water. It was problematic for maintaining hygiene and it still is; cholera and other infectious diseases are a big problem. Poor waste management is another big problem in Lusaka and plastic and other waste covers the streets. So, a group of us started to work on informing and educating our fellow young people in schools and churches on climate change and linking it to the water crisis, hygiene, droughts, and many other issues. Soon we realized that the root cause of contamination of the soil and water was waste, so my colleague and I decided to research waste management. And this is our focus today.

What is your activity now? We have built up a system to collect waste in cities, sell it to recycling companies, and from the money we make, we buy school material and sanitary equipment. We give students lessons in environmentalism and are working very closely with recycling companies – we are setting up proper contracts with them and we audit the quality.

What challenges do you face? There is a lot of bureaucratic obstacles here. For example, we have to get licenses from local authorities which can take months to obtain. There are lots of things we'd like to do, but we are restricted. Sometimes people do business by preferring the 'back door' route where they end up bribing people in offices. This is not the route we take.

What are your dreams? We are running our U-Retain initiative as a non-profit organization now and the word has spread all over the country. We are making an impact and for us, this is a dream come true. We want to be a platform for young people. We want to empower them and let them embrace sustainability.

What is your message to fight plastic pollution in general? Ban single-use-plastic! We have to cut back on the waste we are producing every day. Ultimately it is about education for young people. Because the future belongs to them, and they need to be informed.

SILVER AWARD WINNER
Alejandro Weiss, Valentina Aliaga, Esteban Osses,
Gabriela Carrasco, María José Besoain,
LABVA, Chile

LABVA, CHILE

BIOMATERIALS: A New Cultural Statement

This experimental biomaterials laboratory is located in Valdivia in the south of Chile. Occupying an old building constructed in 1926, LABVA is essentially an independent and self-managed community laboratory and kitchen, where people from the area cook and grow biomaterials and research local and circular economies. LABVA aims to bring science closer to the community, focusing especially on new materials or open biomaterials, and creating a culture around it. Empowering communities and building awareness of the material culture by changing the root issue being the way people consume. Therefore, teaching how to grow, harvest and make materials emotionally binding, associating with the territory, ecosystems and it's communities. Consequently, biomaterials become an agency tool to question matter and its processes.

WE RECOGNIZE: LABVA's main vocation is to reconnect with the territory.

WE CRAFT: LABVA crafts polymers from algae, fish offal, seashell offal, or food waste.

WE COOK: LABVA returns local organic agroindustrial waste back to the productive cycle through the creation of a biomaterial.

WE GROW: LABVA uses biological growth.

WE TEACH: LABVA wants to question the materialities that surround our everyday life in order to understand the processes behind them and therefore practice sovereignty.

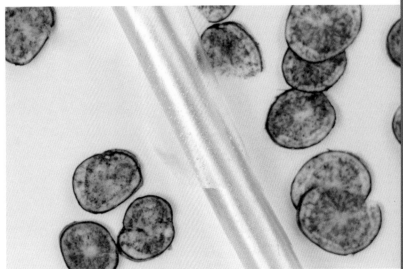

Coffee Talk with Valentina

Please tell us a little about your initiative, Valentina! In 2017, María José, Alejandro and I, founded the Valdivia Biomaterial Laboratory in the south of Chile. They are both architects and I'm a designer. We soon realized that we needed to incorporate a scientific perspective, so we expanded the team to include Esteban, who is a Marine Biologist, and Gabriela, who works in Biochemistry. We explore alternatives to create a native palette of biomaterials. Also, we are a citizens laboratory, which means that we make all of our knowledge, research, and explorations open to citizens. For us, it's also very important to connect with the ancestral culture. There is so much knowledge around that. We think that for creating new materials, we really need to start giving emotion to those materials because the main problem now is that people don't have any attachment to the material culture. If we want to change something, we really need to start giving the material an emotional perspective. Even for the collection process of some raw materials, we have indigenous communities that are dedicated to collecting some fruits in the forest, some abundance that exists in our territory and they do it from a very conscious perspective. We feel we need to start to observe our territories and understand how they interact. When I talk about growing our materials, because we work with living organisms, suddenly we understand that we're no longer a superior entity. We generate certain conditions for the environment but it is the organism that completes the design process. So it's like a co-creation, and that is something very beautiful. We don't have absolute control of what we are growing or how the materials form, it depends on these tiny, tiny organisms.

What was the first step of action for LABVA? It was kind of funny. We are friends and of course we had a lot of common interests. Some of us are interested in local biodiversity, interested in crafts, and manufacturing related to our territorial and ancestral culture. We are mainly interested in food and everything that has to do with cooking in the kitchen, so I think from there, from cooking-related processes like fermentation, we started to question if we were able to experiment mixing our professions with this common interest — using our kitchen and co-creating with living organisms. So we built this biomaterial exercise, this native palette of biomaterial through three key processes for us: The extraction of biopolymers, the cooking of our materials, and the cultivation of biomaterials.

LABVA is a large community now. How did it grow? Because we are in a small city, people became curious. We have a very open approach with our processes and methodologies and we like to share our experience, so people began to wonder "Oh, what's happening here? What is this strange entity talking about biomaterials". We were very focused on the local community and then, suddenly through the media and social networks, we started to grow, to grow and grow. The beautiful thing about LABVA is that people recognize it as a very friendly entity. We want to approach people, to encourage them to get involved. People actually imagine a laboratory as something huge and very far away from us, but in reality, we are just a kitchen that we call a laboratory.

DOPPER, NETHERLANDS

Changemaker Challenge Junior

Dopper, a Dutch social enterprise selling reusable water bottles, is on a mission towards a world with crystal clear water in every ocean and from every tap. They run initiatives like the Dopper Changemaker Challenge Junior, which is an international competition for children aged eight to twelve that challenges them to develop solutions to reduce single-use plastic pollution in the oceans.

Children have unlimited imagination and creativity, which — if guided well — can lead to brilliant solutions. It is important to the Dopper team that children learn that their input is valued and taken seriously. The international competition — held in the UK, the Netherlands, Germany, Belgium, and Nepal — is both accessible for teachers, who can take part with their pupils, and for children independently. Educational materials are provided and designed specifically to guide them every step of the way leading to genius solutions. Children can upload their sketches on the website where the organizers give them the platform they deserve to display their ideas and solutions. Finally, a winner is announced by a jury, and together an actual prototype of their solution is built. This prototype is then displayed in a public place where everyone can see it. The initiative supports teachers' learning objectives and at the same time,

children get the chance to grow and expand their skill set. They develop their creativity, collaboration skills, and readiness to deal with a complex future and embrace a changemaker attitude.

BRONZE AWARD WINNER
Anneke Hendriks, Dopper
Chrissie van Heijnigen, Dopper
Anne Sallaerts, Designathon Works

Coffee Talk with Anneke 🟢 ·||||··||··|·||·||··|··

Firstly, please tell us a bit more about yourself and what you do. My name is Anneke and I live in Haarlem, a city in the Western part of the Netherlands. I am working for Dopper, a social enterprise that sells reusable water bottles. And this bottle is on a mission. We empower people to act in an eco-responsible way by creating awareness campaigns. Within Dopper I am in charge of education, partnerships, and impact investment projects, and have been doing this for a couple of years now.

So what motivated you to work for a social enterprise? I've always been interested in sustainability. After I had been working for a few years, I decided to try and contribute to living more sustainably on a daily basis. I realized that the plastic problem was so big and as an individual, you can feel pretty overwhelmed or powerless at times. What I like about social enterprises is that a lot of them are focused on the solutions instead of the problem in a very creative, entrepreneurial way.

Please tell us a few words about Dopper Changemaker Challenge Junior. This challenge is to empower children to contribute to solutions for the issue of single-use plastics. We guide them by brainstorming to think of a solution. They will sketch out their solution and eventually build a prototype. This can be either a machine or a campaign or an app. They present their prototype and finally, the winner's idea will be implemented in real life. We try to come up with a program that is challenging and fun, but also educational and will inspire as many people as possible. The program runs in the Netherlands, Germany, Belgium, the UK, and Nepal and we plan to branch out all over the world.

What ideas did the children have? A good example of one project was the 'trash bird', which is a drone that flies at night to pick up single-use plastics that are lying on the street. The drone brings it to a garbage bin, and, when it is full, you get a notification so that you can empty it. It flies at night so that people won't think it's fun to throw single-use plastics at it and it's powered by solar energy. So yeah, I would say for a 9 and a 10-year-old child this is pretty innovative and very well done.

Are the parents involved in the program? The children come home and are excited to show their great ideas. Over the dinner table, they convince their parents to use less plastic in the household. This is a great side effect. When you're working with children, you are also working with their parents.

What do you think we all can do to fight plastic pollution on a large scale? Well, the first thing that comes to mind is really action at all levels, big and small. If you are an enterprise, you can take responsibility to innovate and motivate your customers to choose more sustainable options. Buyers can buy more responsibly. It can also go on investment opportunities and start-ups that are working for these calls. On all levels, action is needed. On the positive side, a lot of good things are already happening. Every generation can bring change and should be part of the solution, especially children, because they are so inventive and so creative. That's the first message that we want to spread to the world: Please engage every generation in this topic!

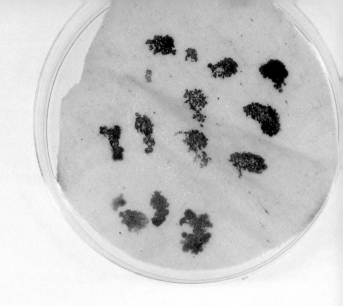
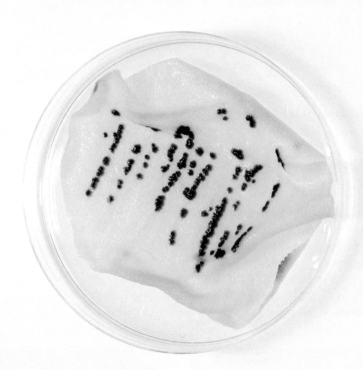
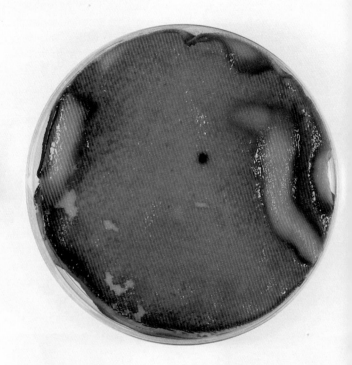

PLANT plASTIC!

This packaging material is alive and contributes to a better environment by growing into a house plant. Learn more on page 18.

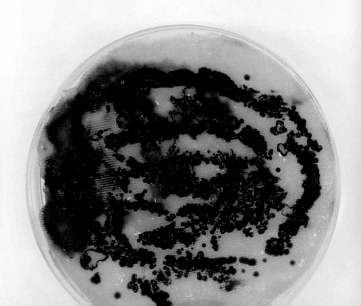

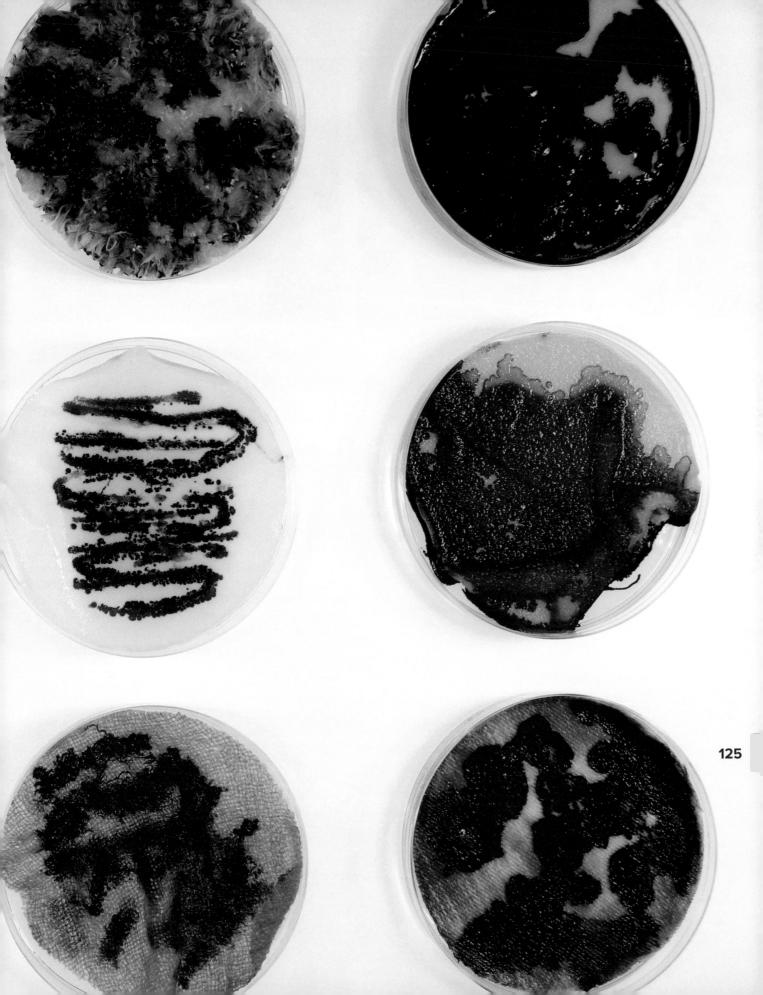

BEYOND PLASTIC.NET

TOP 20

Agustina Besada, Ailén Ortiz, Rocio Gonzales,
Unplastify, Argentina

UNPLASTIFY, ARGENTINA
Let's Unplastify the World

Exploration + Education + Action! This is the motto of the social enterprise Unplastify. The teams are located in Buenos Aires and New York, and are on a mission to change our human relationship with plastic.

In May 2018, the Unplastify team set sail on the sailboat Fanky (named after a song by Charly García) from New York to Gibraltar. They documented the adventurous journey in a logbook. On the high seas, they took plastic samples from the most remote places to contribute to scientific research on ocean plastic pollution. After 27 days at sea covering 3,700 nautical miles, and two stops in Bermuda and the Azores, they reached Gibraltar. In Europe, they interviewed experts and industry leaders to find out their different perspectives and to explore solutions to the problem of plastic waste.

Today Unplastify transforms its experience into action by identifying circular economy solutions and alternatives to disposable plastic. They organize an educational program, the Unplastify Schools Challenge, in South America with the support of National Geographic, adding to its global #PlanetaoPlastico campaign.

Let's change the human relationship with plastic. It is out of control. The problem is not the material but its use and abuse.

Play Together – For a World With Less Plastic!

Martin Angerer created a concept for a playground of to-morrow where children playfully become aware of our responsibility for the environment and a world beyond plastic.

Of course, this playground of the future is plastic-free! The equipment is made of natural materials. The natural joy of interacting together is strengthened by using equipment that only works co-operatively, and where everyone learns about the environment and our responsibility for it. Everybody experiences the co-operative power of learning and participating together. Children learn that when you work as a team you can achieve things that are difficult to reach on your own.

Initiatives such as urban gardening, group exercises on plastic-free fitness equipment, and discussion rounds aim to bring more experienced people to the area. They can share their knowledge, discuss the problems with plastic waste and climate change, and thus create awareness. A lot of questions will be answered at the future plastic-free playground!

Martin Angerer, Max Schwarzlmüller,
Individual Initiative, Austria

127

Eva Smutny, Timm Smutny,
Brigitte Lachmayr, Angela Burgstaller,
Individual Initiative, Austria

INDIVIDUAL INITIATIVE, AUSTRIA

Newstrash

After watching the impressive movie "Plastic Planet" by movie director Werner Boote, Eva Smutny decided to never buy or use plastic garbage bags again. Eva started looking for alternatives and decided to make her own garbage bags from old newspapers. It's a brilliant idea, since the newspaper has already served its main purpose once it has been read. With Eva's idea, it gets reused and is given a second life as a trash bag.

Eva tried out multiple folding techniques and ended up with an ingenious double layer method which proved to be relatively tear-proof and stable. She even went further and experimented until she had the perfect organic glue recipe.

Later on, Eva was looking for an idea to raise money for a charity project together with a group of refugees. They started collecting old newspapers, folding and gluing them together to make garbage bags in all different sizes. People could buy garbage bags for a small donation that helped to finance a temporary apartment for an Iranian family and a couple.

The initiative grew and grew, and Eva and her team were able to financially support refugees in different situations thanks to her initiative. They continue to expand their range of recycled newspaper products to further eliminate unnecessary single-use plastic.

GO ZERO WASTE, SPAIN
Go Zero Waste App

Magda Cebrian and Marti Morató are a couple living in Barcelona who are on a zero-waste journey. They realized that they were missing a tool that could help them to find products, stores, and people to engage with on their journey. They did some research and decided to create their own solution. After a crowdfunding campaign and with the help of an amazing team, the Go Zero Waste app was born in June 2019, on World Ocean's Day!

The Go Zero Waste app helps you to find 'bring your own container' bulk stores, repair cafés, farmers markets, and zero-waste communities to support people on a zero-waste journey. It promotes local products and shops and helps the zero waste community to grow. The ambitious start-up first launched the app in Spain and is working hard to make it available worldwide with ambassadors ready to help in different countries.

The philosophy is to help consumers make more responsible choices, keeping it convenient and local based. The start-up that believes in co-leadership and collaboration seeks to create alliances with people, groups, brands, companies, and public administrations to promote a paradigm shift and move forward together towards a life without waste.

TOP 20

Magda Cebrian, Martí Morató,
App Developer team,
Go Zero Waste, Spain

*From waste ...
to resource.*

Locate bulk shops
near you

Find plastic-free
products

Buy local

Build sustainable
habits

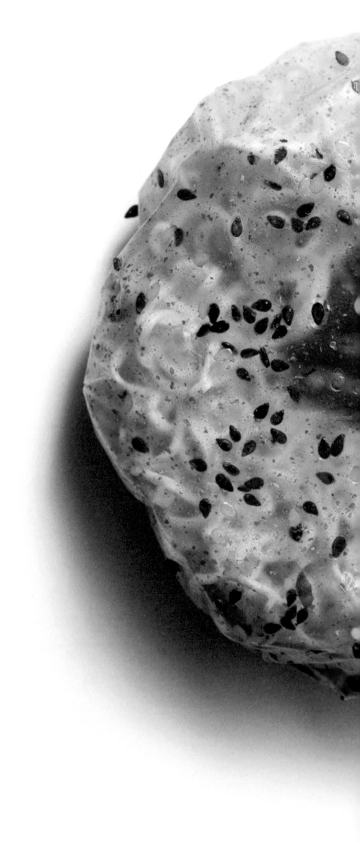

Dissolvable Noodle Packaging

Have you ever thought about the difference between the lifetime of your instant noodles and their packaging? Holly Ground did and invented a dissolvable noodle packaging. Learn more on page 43.

ceero. – Exploring the Circular Economy

TOP 20

Andreas Kissling, Miriam Brüne,
Design Strategist, Germany

Andreas Kissling and Miriam Brüne discovered in their master's thesis that an appropriate business model is the key to a functioning circular economy. Firstly, they analyzed business models in combination with new technologies and their influence on the prevention of electronic and plastic waste. Then they implemented it in a case study.

Andreas and Miriam developed a Product-as-a-Service business model for a dishwasher, taking into account economic, ecological and social interests. To communicate the business model appropriately, they created the fictitious start-up "ceero." which specializes in the rental of large household appliances. The revenue generated would be used to produce radically redesigned equipment based on circular economy principles.

The household products were designed for easy disassembly and remanufacturing to give them a second or even third product life. Whilst ceero. takes full liability for any repairs, the company's products are designed to facilitate and promote self-repair in case of a defect.

With their project, Andreas and Miriam show that economic growth is not exclusively related to new, single-lifetime products and resource extraction. In conclusion, the project serves as a call and a blueprint for manufacturing industries to explore new business models that support a circular economy.

Wise Water

For the beautiful island of Cyprus, its social, economic, and environmental wellbeing is tied strongly to the fate of a single sector; tourism. The future relies on a responsible and sustainable form of tourism. The Wise Water scheme is a result of the increasingly popular reuse movement, which significantly reduces the generation of plastic waste. Making the switch from single-use plastics to reusable alternatives is critically important to the global fight against plastic pollution.

How does Wise Water work? The Cyprus-based start-up is working alongside the Cyprus Sustainable Tourism Initiative and the social media platform Wise Greece to provide high-quality, stainless-steel Wise Water bottles to local businesses. These businesses then agree to provide anyone who comes to their shops with a water bottle – regardless of where it was purchased – with free drinking water refills. The more businesses that sign up, the larger the network of refill points, and the more effective the initiative. Refill points can be found by Wise Water bottle holders in an online app.

The Cypriot-Team first launched the project in local shops in order to create a successful model that can then be replicated to other sectors. For example, the plan is for hotels to provide, refill, take back and sterilize Wise Water bottles for reuse. Participating hotels and tourist accommodations will be certified as Wise Water hotels, and use this as part of a campaign to attract responsible tourism.

Andreas Angeli, Philippos Drousiotis, Melina Taprantzi, Together Cyprus, Cyprus

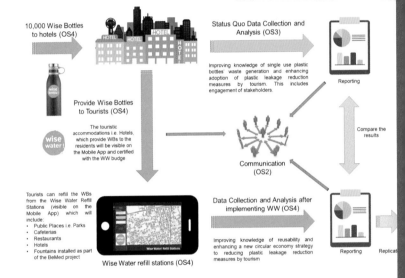

133

UNIVERSITY PROJECT, GERMANY

Sustaim – A Tool for More Sustainability

Sustaim is a mobile application designed to help people balance their environmental footprint, and to show them personalized options for action. The smartphone app is based on the idea of using a positive form of knowledge and information transfer to create social transformation. The focus is on presenting abstract information in an understandable way and showing which possibilities one has as an individual within the personal scope of action.

The application comprises of three different functions:

1. A balancing tool that uses a holistic calculation method to provide information about the effects of one's own impact on the environment.

2. An area that shows personalized alternatives for action based on one's own ecological footprint.

3. A collection of facts, in which scientifically proven, important developments and interrelationships are presented in a short, concise, and appealing way.

As a mobile solution, Sustaim represents a new approach to help create awareness and knowledge of how to gradually integrate it into everyday life.

Tebeya Leicht, Monika Litzinger,
Interaction Designer,
HfG Schwäbisch Gmünd, Germany

INDIVIDUAL INITIATIVE, ITALY
Plastic-free Venice

In August 2019, the environmental initiative Venice Lagoon Plastic Free carried out a point sampling study of the water in the Grand Canal in Venice. They conducted a preliminary qualitative analysis aimed at detecting micropollutants related to the presence of plastics in the marine environment. The water samples were then analyzed, where bulk water and vapor phase were both subjected to Solid Phase Micro Extraction, Gas Chromatography and Mass Spectrometry (SPME-GC- MS) analysis in the laboratories of ITT Montani in Fermo, the oldest analytical institute in Italy. The analytical strategy used to determine the molecular fingerprint of Venice's lagoon water is environmentally friendly as no toxic solvent is used.

The year 2020, with the absence of mass tourism due to Covid-19, allowed for an interesting extension to the scientific project. The same study had been replicated to analyze Venice waterways during the Covid-19 lockdown to compare possible differences. The team is currently working on the test results.

Dr. Davide Poletto, Prof. Teresa Cecchi, Italy

Charles Hambayi, Christopher Banda
Derrick Munsele, Individual Initiative, Zambia

INDIVIDUAL INITIATIVE, ZAMBIA

Plant a Fruit Tree!

Charles Hambayi is a graduate in Environmental Science and Natural Resources Management from the University of Zambia. After graduating from University, he was keen to come up with a solution for solving some of the environmental challenges the world is facing, such as plastic pollution and deforestation.

In 2017, Charles started a plant seeding project, where he used empty plastic bottles as plant pots for his exotic and indigenous fruit tree seedlings. Charles also started to plant vegetables in empty plastic sacks and bottles. Since then, he and his friends have been selling their fruit trees, and some have even been donated to schools. In 2018, during the celebration for world environment day, they donated 300 fruit tree seedlings to be planted at various schools. Charles has an ambitious goal ahead: He wants to plant one million fruit trees by 2025!

ECOINS, COSTA RICA

An Eco-Currency Encouraging Us To Recycle

The e-currency "ecoins" is a response to the great challenge we have as a society. It is a virtual eco-coin that rewards commitment to recycling. Ecoins are awarded in exchange for recoverable waste that has been either collected at home by local communities or taken to authorized reception centers. Awarded points are deposited into a virtual wallet that offers the user the option to exchange them for discount coupons for eco-responsible products and services. The waste collected is later reintroduced into the production cycle as raw material.

The business model of ecoins changes the traditional way of dealing with waste management. It transforms it from an expensive and complicated environmental problem to an alternative that offers economic opportunities through a strategic alliance of digital communication platforms, social networks, and citizen participation. It has the ability to educate people on environmental issues and waste management while creating economic incentives that encourage consumers to take responsibility for their waste.

Ecoins is currently present in Costa Rica, Panama, Peru, Guatemala, and El Salvador. The start-up's objective is to grow the concept throughout the Latin American region and beyond.

Lucila Espinoza, Karla Chaves,
ecoins, Costa Rica

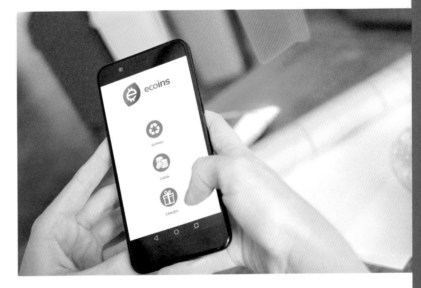

137

Foamation

This sustainable foam is made from glass and egg shells. It is not only decorative, but it also has impressive sound insulation capabilities. Learn more about Steven Akoun's innovative wall tiles on page 33.

139

LESS PLASTIC

Dawamoru Fernandez, Aitor San Francisco,
Bilibin Circular, Spain

BILIBIN CIRCULAR, SPAIN

Less Plastic Certificate

Less Plastic is a certificate that helps companies to eliminate single-use plastic from their products, services, and processes.

The Less Plastic Certificate is awarded after a series of steps have been completed in which the company shows that it considerably eliminates its waste and single-use plastic. The rationale is to divide a company, community, or process into several action areas. In those action areas, all the places where single-use plastic is used are identified. Having identified the areas of action, a plan, similar to that of an onion with multiple skins, is developed. Within this unique methodology, there are several 'layers' of action, and it is the responsibility of the company or community how deep it wants to go. There are a few mandatory criteria that must be met to eliminate single-use plastic, and there are other optional points related to wider social and environmental aspects that the organization can consider.

After developing an action plan, having implemented the practices, and measured the results, the company will eventually avoid the use of single-use plastics. This will make it a more sustainable company with a clear roadmap towards total sustainability.

EVERYDAY PLASTIC, UNITED KINGDOM

The Everyday Plastic Survey

After moving to a village where no plastic recycling was available, Daniel Webb decided to conduct a little experiment – he collected every piece of plastic waste he generated for a whole year. After counting, categorizing, analyzing, and photographing the 4,490 items, he was commissioned to make a giant mural before co-authoring a seminal report; 'What we throw away and where it goes' with academic researcher Dr. Julie Schneider. The project attracted extensive national and international press coverage and was the launchpad for Everyday Plastic, the organization Daniel founded in 2018.

Everyday Plastic has taken David Webb on a unique personal journey, and this experience led to the launch of a new project – The Everyday Plastic Survey. The concept is simple, the Everyday Plastic Survey challenges participants to collect and record a week's worth of their household plastic waste before submitting their data to receive their personalized plastic footprint. This footprint provides a comprehensive breakdown of what they throw away and where it goes. Alongside their personal plastic footprint, the initiative offers their participants straightforward advice, easy-to-apply tips, and relevant resources to support their switch to a less-plastic life. It is specifically designed to be a fun and interactive way to connect individuals with the global plastic problem and to mobilize a new wave of environmental campaigners.

Daniel Webb, Dr. Julie Schneider,
Everyday Plastic, United Kingdom

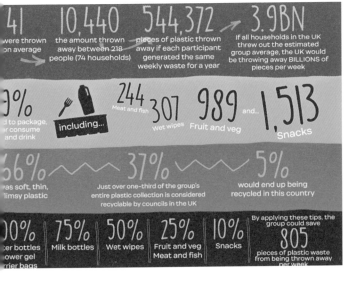

DAMN PLASTIC, AUSTRIA
Damn Plastic

Victoria Neuhofer, Stephanie Sinko,
Damn Plastic, Austria

*Plastic is not the enemy,
but our mindset is.*

The goal of Damn Plastic: Ban Single-Use Plastic Within ONE Generation.

Damn Plastic was founded in Salzburg, Austria by two passionate women to change our planet A.

They created:
A Zero-Waste event management company.
A plastic-free store in the heart of Salzburg.
A franchise system for young people.
A certification for plastic-free events.
A plastic-free packaging solution company.
A modern start-up, built to make a difference and making plastic-free partying possible.

INDIVIDUAL INITIATIVE, INDIA
Chilika Junior Rangers

Chilika, located on India's east coast, is the largest brackish water lagoon in the world. It is also the largest wintering ground for migratory birds on the Indian subcontinent, hosting over 160 species of birds that travel up to 12,000 km in the peak migratory season. The lake is home to a number of threatened species of plants and animals and is an important ecosystem for marine life.

Thousands of daily visitors along with local inhabitants create a lot of waste that is not properly disposed of and eventually finds its way into the lake. The Chilika Junior Rangers project intends to create awareness, provide solutions, and help to save the Chilika lake and the special Irrawaddy dolphins found there.

It is rightly said that education is the most powerful weapon, so local environmentalists actively engage with schools, colleges, and the local community. Their goal is to educate the youth who will in turn will educate their families.

The initiative creates enthusiastic teams of school children called "Chilika Junior Rangers". Being proud members of the Chilika Junior Rangers, these children play a vital role in shaping the community. Each Junior Ranger takes over the responsibility of his or her own Ranger house and surroundings to ensure that it is clean. Tutors visit schools and share their knowledge about the sources of plastic waste. The project serves as a role model for other neighboring villages.

Shagun Kar, Aurobindo Stitapragyan,
Individual Initiative, India

143

Algae Pattern

Working without color is impossible for textile designer Maria Mayer. That's why she found a way to reuse the water that has already been dyed in the textile production to produce a printing paste. Learn more on page 23.

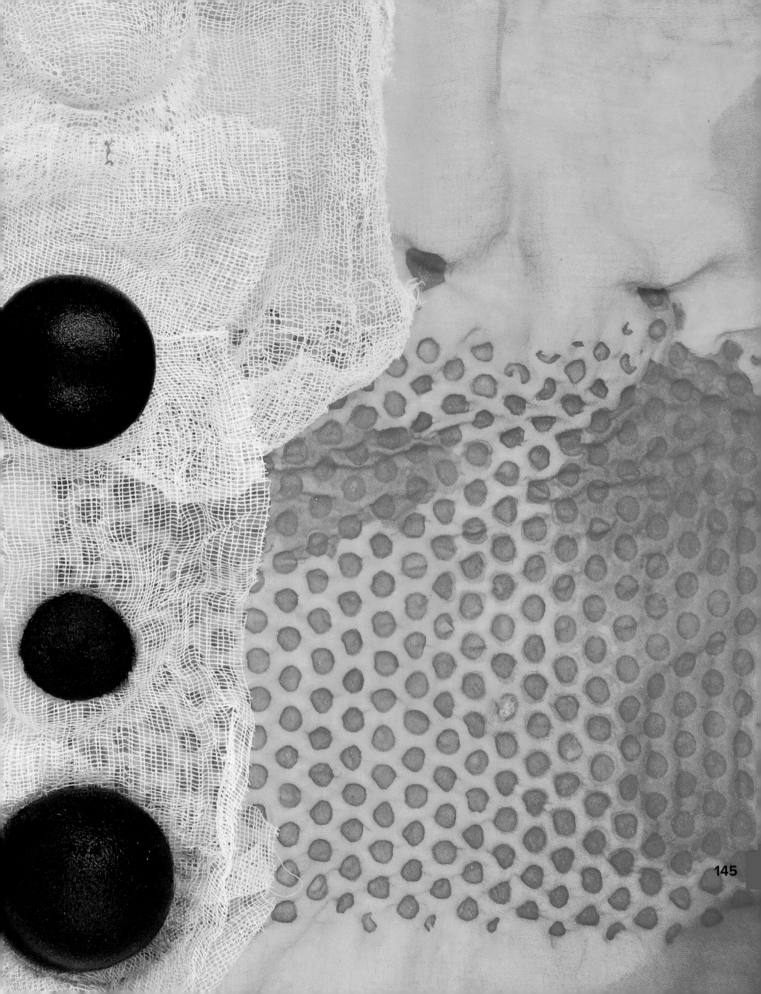

NewPa – Immersions with Econscience

The NewPa project stems from the search for an innovative, educational offering based on Environmental Awareness and Sustainability, Education in Values and Linguistic Immersion in English and Spanish. NewPa creators Mónica, Bruno, and Rash believe that education is the basis of all change in our strive for a sustainable world.

NewPa, therefore, is an initiative that coveys the importance of values and looking after nature while having fun in an experimental learning environment. The founders coined the term 'Econscience' based on the following principles:

1. The creation of materials for and during the educational programs is based on a sustainable process that fulfills the commitment to promote a circular economy.
2. All the staff firmly believe in the project and this helps the educators become genuine role models to the children. The educators are paid above industry average salaries and their well-being is of place great importance.
3. The initiative works towards providing fair prices for customers.
4. A healthy and responsible diet is essential in understanding the importance of sustainability.
5. The English Immersion activities are aimed at Spanish children and they plan to hold Summer Camps in Spanish for foreign children.

NewPa is in the process of becoming an Association as it continues to grow little by little. With each step, the passionate founders incorporate new workshops and experiences for the children, and upcoming activities are also aimed at adults, teenagers, and families.

Mónica Pérez-Solero Labiaga,
Bruno Torcal, Rash Silva,
NewPa, Spain

Let's Do It in India

Let's Do It India, founded by Pankaj Choudhary, is the Indian offshoot of the Let's Do It! World organization. They aim to reduce the problem of illegally dumped waste and conduct regular clean-up activities.

The parent organization, 'Let's Do It! World', has been working on environmental conservation projects for several years by mobilizing millions of positive-minded, action-orientated people and using innovative technological solutions to deal with waste issues. Every September, on World Cleanup Day, people in 150 countries stand up against the global waste problem and clean up trash, making it the biggest positive civic action in the world. This creates an epic green wave that begins in New Zealand and travels around the world, with millions of volunteers taking action in their country as the day passes through their time zone, before ending in Hawaii. A key motive of Let's Do It India is to promote a greater understanding of the connections between people and their environment and to encourage creative thinking through hands-on education of waste management.

The enthusiastic people in this initiative empower their communities to protect and preserve the habitat through environmental education and creative exploration. Core to their beliefs is the notion that people want to do the right thing; all they need is a little encouragement or incentive. Clean-ups alone will not solve the waste crisis, but these events inspire positive change in society. They promote changes in individual behavior, create awareness of waste management and draw civil society's and government's attention to this crisis.

Abhishek Kumar Patel, Pankaj Choudhary, Ravi Pratap Singh,
Let's Do It India, India

147

Water resistance of MSU-Tech

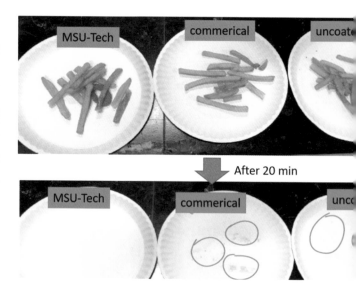

A closed-loop and sustainable approach for the fabrication of plastic-free oil- and water-resistant paper products

UNIVERSITY PROJECT, UNITED STATES

Plastic-Free Paper Products Resistant to Oil and Water

The majority of today's oil and water-resistant cardboard used in food packaging contains coatings of plastic or layers of metal which inhibits proper recycling.

In their scientific study, Muhammad Rabnawaz and Zhao Li from Michigan State University developed a green, unique and facile approach for the fabrication of grease and water-resistant paper products with 100 % recyclability.

Now it gets scientific: Low surface energy polydimethylsiloxane (PDMS) was grafted onto a biobased chitosan polymer via urea linkages to prepare the graft copolymer chitosan-graft-polydimethylsiloxane (chitosan-g-PDMS). Chitosan-g-PDMS was then applied as a coating onto an unbleached Kraft paper substrate from an aqueous solution. The coated paper substrates exhibited good hydrophobic properties with a water contact angle of $120.53 \pm 0.96°$ and a Cobb 60 value of $9.89 \pm 0.32 \, g/m^2$. The coated paper substrates also showed good oil-resistance. The tensile strength, crushing resistance, bending stiffness, and internal tearing resistance of the paper before and after coating treatment was determined. Scanning electron microscopy (SEM) analysis was used to characterize changes in the porosity of the paper before and after the coating. The pulp recyclability of the coated paper was validated by subjecting the coated paper samples to repulping and washing treatment.

This novel and practical approach can provide significant environmental benefits by offering plastic-free, fluorine-free and fully-recyclable water- and grease-resistant paper; thus promoting sustainability due to its unique closed-loop approach.

Muhammad Rabnawaz, Zhao Li,
Individulal Initiative, United States

Replace Plastic Bags by Textile Bags

For many developing countries, coast waste is a major concern. There a three major reasons why single-use plastic is still used on a large scale: Low cost of plastic, simple availability, and low weight of the material. This project, initiated by Ravi Pratap Singh, centers around the manufacture and reuse of textile cloth bags instead of single-use plastic bags. Here is how it works:

1. Used clothes are collected through a national campaign and used for manufacturing. There are cloth collection centers at local colleges so that clothes can be collected and segregated for further processing.
2. The materials are washed and dried in an environmentally responsible way.
3. The tailoring is done locally to put people back to work and to support fair manual work.
4. The bags are distributed through schools and colleges and across local markets. This way the mission reaches each and every house.

The outcome of the initiative is that, by using cloth from houses across the country, conservation of fiber, resource, and plant wealth in India is achieved. Plastic bags are avoided and people are employed which also improves society and security.

The cloth bags are cost-efficient; they have a much longer product life than plastic bags, they are stronger, washable, biodegradable, easy to carry, and locally available.

Ravi Pratap Singh,
Individual Initiative, India

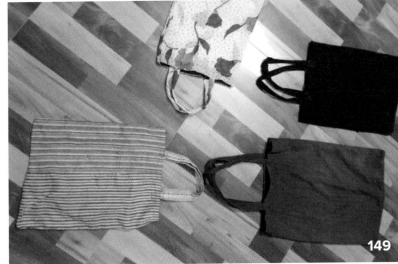

TIPS FOR BOOKWORMS

WHY MATERIALS MATTER
by Seetal Solanki

Responsible Design
for a Better World

Why
Materia
Matter

Responsible Design
for a Better World

Seetal Solanki

MATERIAL REVOLUTION
by Sascha Peters

Sustainable and Multi-Purpose
Materials for Design and Architecture

Lo-TEK
Design by Radical Indigenism
by Julia Watson

Natural Wisdom from Traditional
Ecological Knowledge

STUFF MATTERS
by Mark Miodownik

Exploring the Marvelous Materials
That Shape Our Man-Made World

MATERIALS IN PROGRESS
Innovations for Designers & Architects
by Diana Drewes & Sascha Peters

Examples for a New Mindfulness and
Conscious Consumption

LESSONS LEARNED

BEYONDPLASTIC started in 2019 and is still a young movement. These are the lessons we've learned so far:

1. There is a movement. We came into contact with amazing people working passionately for a world with less plastic. There are so many creative ideas, concepts, products, and initiatives out there as the BEYONDPLASTIC Award demonstrates. It is so good to see that all these enthusiastic people engage in multiple disciplines with different backgrounds, interests, resources, methods, and philosophies, because we don't think that there is only ONE smart idea or invention which will make the breakthrough in solving the plastic pollution problem.

2. Reducing plastic consumption is a complex matter. It needs technical solutions but even more importantly, it needs a social and cultural change. The technical language used can be confusing and many companies manufacturing and using single-use plastic tell stories of self-interest and misuse information for manipulative greenwashing.

3. There is a need for a platform to connect, educate, clarify and show what great solutions are already existing and what is possible in the future. We are dedicated to growing the BEYONDPLASTIC platform in order to connect people and their brilliant ideas and to spread this important and good news across the world. The great thing is, that we act financially and politically independent giving us freedom, authenticity, and effectiveness. We are on a long run. Ironically we have to because overcoming plastoholism is a mission for generations. But we are confident. We face a problem we humans created. So we can and we have to fix it.

OUR MESSAGE TO COMPANIES

Sustainable design only works as a holistic approach. It has to be embedded in the company culture and to be lived and breathed in every aspect. It is amazing to see young designers and start-ups having the courage to do this by using methods as circular design, cradle-to-cradle, or biofabrication.

For an eco-responsible business, the Golden Rules of Sustainability REDUCE – REUSE – RECYCLE are a good guideline. They have to be prioritized exactly in this order.

Plastic recycling has to be looked at critically. It is a downcycling process, meaning you can make a gray park bench out of transparent PET bottles but not vice versa. Today, recycling doesn't work well logistically and energetically, and the recycling rate today is low, being in a single-digit percentage rate. More recycling in the future would be good, but we don't see it as the salvation of the plastic pollution problem.

With every piece of plastic, we can only do three things:

1. Burn it and at least get energy out of it (but at the cost of a high carbon-footprint),
2. Pollute land and sea or
3. Downcycle it. It will always remain plastic.

Established companies have to put their narrow, short-term financial focus aside and make a cultural shift with strict authenticity and credibility. It is not enough to put 'recyclable' labels on conventional packages and add some organic ingredients to call it 'bioplastic'. Today's well-educated and well-connected consumers will watch very closely to see if companies are taking their journey towards sustainability seriously and honestly. Just jumping on the bandwagon and running a fancy greenwashing campaign will backfire. Eco-consciousness is not just a trend. It is a movement leading to a cultural change. Technology, when used wisely, will be a helpful tool to make that change.

OUR MESSAGE TO YOU AS AN EARTHLING

The good news is that we are becoming aware that we have a plastic pollution problem. Now it is time to take the next step and act – use less plastic!

We have to realize that we are more than consumers. We are responsible people who can make our own choices.

We have to re-connect with the things which surround us and which we use. We should ask:

Where do the raw materials come from?
Under which labor conditions were they made?
What do they contain?
Were animals mistreated?
Where will they end up after use?

Only then should we make our purchasing decisions based on the answers to these questions. Let us be curious and explore the stories behind products. If the story is bad, stay away from it!

Let us rediscover the aesthetic culture behind materials. For example, there is a hundreds of years old rich history behind drinking our beverages out of beautiful glass and ceramic containers. A couple of years ago mankind started nipping at plastic bottles and straws like infants. What did we gain? Let us put quality in front of quantity again.

Let us return to responsible packaging. It just doesn't make any sense to wrap our food, personal care, and household products which we use within days in materials that will remain in the world for centuries.

When engineers started playing with plastic around 70 years ago and designed throw-away products, nobody imagined the problems they cause today. But today we know. It's like a train on a track that goes faster and faster until it will derail. We just have to put it in the right tempo again. Let us fix our plastoholic behavior!

THANK YOU FOR BEING ON BOARD!

As accountable citizens of Spaceship Earth, it is our duty to act as conscientious individuals. As a guidance we have spun the circular economy mantra of REDUCE-REUSE-RECYCLE further by adding two more R's:

REFUSE
REDUCE
REUSE
REPAIR
RECYCLE

153

THE STORY OF THIS BOOK

When we saw so many great ideas for a world with less plastic participating in the BEYONDPLASTIC Award, we knew immediately that we had to put them in print and show them to the world. And not just any ordinary print, but the finest, high-quality print, because we are print aficionados.

It was an enjoyable and rewarding process. From selecting materials, binding book dummies, talking to suppliers, working on text and layout, and finally standing at the printing press, seeing the sheets gaining life, and smelling fresh paper and ink. We hope this passion was captured in our book and you can feel it when browsing through it.

We would like to thank all our contributors and thanks to YOU for holding this book in your hands.

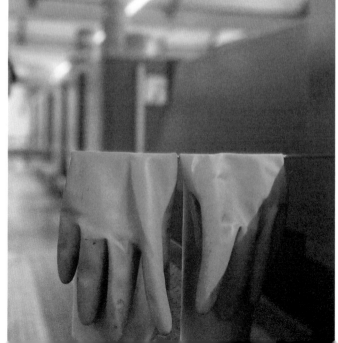

THE 'BOOKMAKERS'

The Publisher
As an engineer, entrepreneur, and artist, Ulrich dreams of a cultural evolution and a natural material renaissance in order to fix our relationship with single-use-plastic. Consequently, he created a platform where passionate people on this mission can exchange their ideas and concepts.

The Printesse
Jessi knows exactly which book will be launched when — not only because her third generation, family-run business prints them — but also because she enjoys filling up her bookshelf at home.

The Creative Everything Officer
Dani is a Color & Design Lover with a passion for printed products and executing bold ideas. For her, a good, beautiful book is soul food in our fast-paced, digital world.

The Communicator
Katie is an experienced marketing specialist and is passionate about helping sustainable brands grow. She is the community manager of the BEYONDPLASTIC platform.

TABLE OF CONTENTS

MOST BEAUTIFUL SOLUTION

BEST INITIATIVE

MADE IN EUROPE
BY GREAT PEOPLE,
HANDCRAFTED WITH
PASSION FOR
BOOKMAKING.

100 % ORGANIC MATERIAL
KEEP AWAY FROM PLASTIC
DO NOT GREENWASH
HAND OUT TO FRIENDS
ENJOY READING

COLOPHON

© 2021 BEYONDPLASTIC
ISBN 978-3-00-067649-9

All rights reserved. No image or part of this book may be reproduced in any form or by any means without the written permission of the author.

BEYONDPLASTIC is an ongoing initiative. If you have any feedback, we would love to hear from you. Just send an e-mail to hello@beyondplastic.net.

Publisher & Distributor
BEYONDPLASTIC
Friedrich-Ebert-Str. 25
D-61476 Kronberg
www.beyondplastic.net

Editor
Ulrich Krzyminski

PR & Marketing
Cocoon Communications
www.cocooncommunications.co.uk

Concept, Design & Production Management
Daniela Louise Heinemann
www.daniela-heinemann.de

Typeface
Proxima Nova

Photo Credits
BEYONDPLASTIC Award Participants
The Bookmakers

Print
Wahl-Druck GmbH
www.wahl-druck.de

Paper
PERGRAPHICA Natural Rough, 120g/m²

Bookbinding
Buchbinderei Schaumann GmbH
www.buchbinderei-schaumann.de

Circulation
First Edition 1,000 copies